Numeracy

Level 2

D0191726

Su Nicholson

Consultant **John Elkington**

About this book

This book has been written to support you in taking the Adult Numeracy Level 2 test. The authors are experienced teachers and examiners who know the sorts of questions that are usually asked in the test.

How to use this book

The book is arranged into sections which cover the Adult Numeracy Level 2 criteria. Each section starts with a list of what you should already know and what you will learn. Use this list to check your progress.

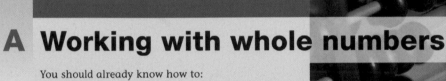

A Working with whole numbers

You should already know how to:

✓ read, write, order and compare numbers

Each section is broken down into smaller topics. Each topic starts with 'First read this...' which outlines all the skills you need to know.

1 Place value and rounding

First read this ...

The 'Now try it!' heading starts off the exercise, giving you plenty of practice at the key techniques. The questions are mainly set in context as in the actual test, so that you get relevant practice throughout.

Now try it!

1. A large company announces annual profits of £23 billion.
   Write the number 23 billion in figures.

The CD icon in the margin points you to additional learning material on the free Hot Topics CD-ROM included with this book.

At the end of each section, to help you remember what you have learned, 'First complete this...' repeats the important information from the section, leaving out key words. Try to fill in the words then look back through the section to check you are correct.

First complete this ...

▷ An integer is a _____ _____.

The final 'Now try it!' of the section consists of practice test questions in multiple-choice format so you can practise for the real thing.

Contents

A Working with whole numbers

You should already know how to:

✔ read, write, order and compare numbers

✔ recognise negative numbers.

By the end of this section you will know how to:

▷▷ round numbers

▷▷ use factors to simplify calculations

▷▷ use estimation to check calculations

▷▷ use inverse calculations to check answers.

1 Place value and rounding

First read this ...

In the decimal number system all integers are made from the ten digits:
0, 1, 2, 3, 4, 5, 6, 7, 8, 9.

> **Remember**
>
> An **integer** is a whole number.

▷ The value of each digit in a number depends on its position in the number, its **place value**.

This place-value table shows the number seventeen thousand and sixty-three.

Billions	Hundred millions	Ten millions	Millions	Hundred thousands	Ten thousands	Thousands	Hundreds	Tens	Units
					1	7	0	6	3

You leave a gap or use a comma between groups of three digits.

You write this number as 17 063 or 17,063.

Large numbers are often rounded.

▷ To round a number:

  ▷ Count along to the last digit that is needed.

  ▷ If the next digit is 5, 6, 7, 8 or 9, round the last digit up.

  ▷ If the next digit is 0, 1, 2, 3 or 4, leave the last digit.

Example 1: 25 687 people watch a rugby match.
Round this number to the nearest thousand.

Write the number in a place-value table.

Billions	Hundred millions	Ten millions	Millions	Hundred thousands	Ten thousands	Thousands	Hundreds	Tens	Units
					2	5	6	8	7

The number in the hundreds column is 6, so round the thousands digit up.

Answer: 26 000

Example 2: A newspaper reported that approximately 150 000 people attended the Glastonbury festival in 2005. What are the possible values of the attendance?

Write the number in a place-value table.

Billions	Hundred millions	Ten millions	Millions	Hundred thousands	Ten thousands	Thousands	Hundreds	Tens	Units
				1	5	0	0	0	0

Assume the number is rounded to the nearest ten thousand.
You can show the rounded number on a number line:

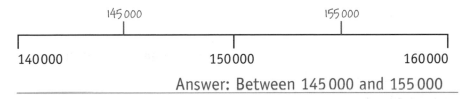

Answer: Between 145 000 and 155 000

▶▶ *Now try it!*

1. A large company announces annual profits of £23 billion.
   Write the number 23 billion in figures.

   _____

2. Our galaxy contains roughly 250 000 000 000 stars.
   How many billion is this?

   _____

3. One of the largest lotto wins was £22 590 829.
   Round this amount to the nearest £100 000.

   _____

4. In 2005–2006 the average attendance at a premiership football match was 34 000 to the nearest 1 000.
   What was the smallest possible average attendance?

   _____

5. A population of 3.5 million bacteria increases by 488 000.
   How many bacteria are there now?

   _____

> **Remember**
>
> A **billion** is one thousand million.
> 1 billion = 1 000 000 000 or 10^9

First read this ...

Negative numbers are used for:

- temperatures below zero
- heights below sea level
- company losses
- overdrawn bank accounts.

▷ To find the **difference** between two numbers:

  ▷ If the signs are the same, **subtract** the numbers.

  ▷ If the signs are different, **add** the numbers.

> **Example 1:** A minimum temperature of –88°C was recorded in Antarctica.
> Moscow recorded one of their lowest overnight temperatures of –31°C.
> What is the difference between the two temperatures?

The lower of the two temperatures is –88°C.
Sketch a number line.

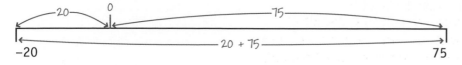

The signs are the same.

You find the difference by subtracting: 88 – 31 = 57.

Answer: 57 degrees

> **Example 2:** A girl has an overdraft of £20 on her bank account.
> How much must she pay in, so that the balance is £75?

Remember

A **loss** or **overdraft** is a **negative** amount of money.

The overdrawn balance is –£20.

Sketch a number line.

The signs are different.

You find the difference by adding: 20 + 75 = 95.

Answer: £95

▶▶ Now try it!

1. On one night in London the temperature fell to 12°C.
   On the same night in Moscow the temperature fell to –5°C.
   What was the difference in temperature?

   _____

2. A boy started the month with a balance of –£25 in his
   bank account. He paid £120 out of his account during the
   month but did not put any money into his account.
   What was his balance at the end of the month?

   _____

3. A company reported a loss of £10 million in 2004.
   In 2005 it reported a profit of £3 million.
   What is the difference between the two amounts?

   _____

   Remember

   A **profit** or **credit** is a
   positive amount of money.

4. The boiling point of krypton is –152°C.
   The boiling point of radon is –65°C.
   What is the difference between the two boiling points?

   _____

5. In 3 months US energy giant Enron, went from a company
   with assets of £62bn to a company with debts of £18bn.
   What is the difference between these two amounts?

   _____

   Remember

   Assets are recorded as positive
   amounts.

6. The highest recorded temperature in the UK is 39°C. The
   lowest recorded temperature in the UK is –27°C. What is
   the difference between these two temperatures?

   _____

7. A bank allows university students a £1 000 overdraft
   facility on their bank accounts. In one month a student
   was £675 overdrawn. The next month the same student
   was £730 overdrawn. What is the difference between these
   two amounts?

   _____

3 Factors and multiples

Multiplications and divisions can be broken down into stages using **factors**.

For example, 3 × 2 = 6 so multiplying by 6 is the same as multiplying by 3 and then by 2.

▷ The **factors** of a number are the numbers that will divide into it exactly.

For example, the factors of 12 are: 1, 2, 3, 4, 6, 12.

▷ A **prime number** has exactly two factors: itself and 1. The first five prime numbers are 2, 3, 5, 7 and 11.

You can write a number as the product of its **prime factors** using a **factor tree**.

| **Example:** Write 48 as the product of its prime factors. |

Draw a factor tree. Split up the numbers into factor pairs until you have only prime numbers at the ends of the 'branches'.

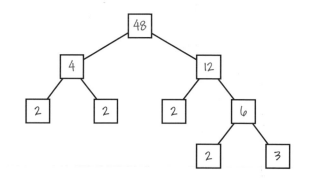

Answer: 48 = 2 × 2 × 2 × 2 × 3 = 2^4 × 3

2 is a factor of 48, so 48 is a **multiple** of 2.

▷ A **multiple** of a number can be divided exactly by that number.

For example, 8, 12 and 16 are all multiples of 4.

Here are some quick ways of checking for factors and multiples:

- 2 is a factor of even numbers ending in 0, 2, 4, 6, or 8
- 3 is a factor when the digits add up to 3, 6 or 9
- 5 is a factor when the number ends in 5 or 0
- 9 is a factor when the digits add up to 9
- 10 is a factor when the number ends in a 0.

Tip

1 × 12, 2 × 6 and 3 × 4 are all the possible *factor pairs* of 12.

Remember

A **product** is the result of a multiplication.

Tip

Check that each branch of your factor tree ends with a prime number.

Tip

2^4 = 2 × 2 × 2 × 2

Tip

Keep adding the digits until you get a single digit.

▶▶ Now try it!

1. Write each of these numbers as a product of its prime factors. The factor trees have been started for you.

a
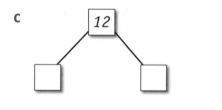

b

96

c

12

d

162

2. Write down which of these numbers are multiples of:

A 2   B 3   C 5   D 9

The first one is done for you.

a 78   *A and B*

b 145 _____   c 261 _____

d 523 _____   e 630 _____

f 936 _____   g 1275 _____

h 3147 _____   i 6795 _____

Estimating and checking

First read this ...

You can improve your accuracy if you check your answers.

There are two main methods: using estimation and using inverse calculations.

▷ You can estimate by rounding to one significant figure (s.f.).

126 = 100 to 1 s.f.   5.37 = 5 to 1 s.f.   87 = 90 to 1 s.f.

Example 1: A student rents a bedsit for £58 a week. Approximately how much will he pay for the year?

You need to work out 58 × 52.

Round each number to 1 s.f.: 60 × 50.

60 × 50 = 6 × 5 × 10 × 10 = 30 × 100 = 3 000

Answer: £3 000

Try to choose numbers with common factors in division problems.

Example 2: A conversion from euros to pounds is €1 = 69 p. Approximately how many euros are equivalent to £140?

You first need to change the pounds to pence by multiplying by 100.

140 × 100 = 14 000 pence

Every 69 p is €1 so you need to work out $\frac{14\,000}{69}$.

It is not helpful to round both numbers to 1 s.f.

69 = 70 to 1 s.f. and 7 is a factor of 14.

The calculation is $\frac{14\,000}{70} = \frac{1\,400}{7} = 200$

Answer: €200

You should check that your answer makes sense. For example, you know that €1 = 69 p so £1 is more than €1 and £140 is more than €140.

▷ You can use an **inverse calculation** to check answers.

Example 3: Twenty-five students each pay 48 pence for a college magazine. What is the total amount spent, in pounds? Use an inverse calculation to check your answer.

The total amount spent in pence = 25 × 48. To change pence to pounds, divide by 100.

The calculation is shown in the flowchart.

25 → │ × 48p │ → │ ÷ 100 │ → £12   i.e. $\frac{25 \times 48}{100} = 12$

Check: Start with £12 and do the inverse calculations to arrive back at 25.

25 ← │ ÷ 48p │ ← │ × 100 │ ← £12   i.e. $\frac{12 \times 100}{48} = 25$

Tip

Breaking numbers into factors makes it easier to calculate.

Tip

Make sure the quantities are in the same units.

Tip

+ is inverse to −
× is inverse to ÷

▶▶ *Now try it!*

1. The cost of a holiday for 42 students is £9 875. By rounding each number to the nearest 10, estimate the cost of the holiday for each student.

    _____

2. A man spends £23 per week on travel. Approximately how much would he spend on travel in two years?

    _____

3. A dressmaker buys 62 feet of material. 1 foot = 12 inches and 1 metre is approximately 40 inches. Approximately how many metres of material does she buy?

    _____

4. Approximately how many miles is equivalent to 162 km? Use the conversion 5 miles is approximately 8 km.

    _____

    In questions 5–8, draw a flowchart to show the calculation and the inverse calculation you need to do to check the result.

5. Popcorn costs £3 at the cinema. The cinema sells 65 lots of popcorn and receives £195.

    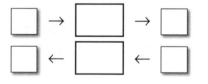

6. Six friends go out for a meal to celebrate a girl's birthday. Her five friends decide to treat the girl to the meal. The cost per person is £25. The friends calculate they each need to pay £30 to cover the total cost.

    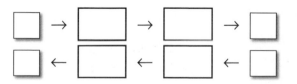

7. A boy buys 500 oranges for £75 and sells them for 20p each. He calculates that he makes a profit of £25.

    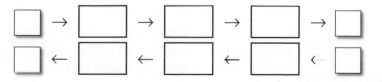

5 Tips for calculating

Here are some tips to help you do calculations.

1   You can **calculate change** by **counting up** from the cost.

> **Example 1:** A woman's bill in the supermarket is £17.85. How much change does she receive from a £20 note?

Count up from £17.85 to £20.

£17.85 + 5p = £17.90

£17.90 + 10p = £18

£18 + £2 = £20

Total change = 5p + 10p + £2 = £2.15

Answer: £2.15

> **Tip**
>
> Imagine the number line:
>
>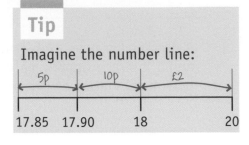

2   You can use the **number line** to help with **subtraction**.

> **Example 2:** Calculate 8 000 – 276.

Subtracting 276 is the same as subtracting 200 then 70 then 6, using the partitioning method.

Answer: 7 724

> **Tip**
>
> This is particularly useful when you are subtracting from a number ending in zeros.

3   You can use **factors** to **mutiply** and **divide**.

▷   4 = 2 × 2: to divide by 4, divide by 2 then divide by 2 again.

▷   5 = 10 ÷ 2: to divide by 5, first multiply by 2 then divide by 10.

4   You can use **partitioning** for **long multiplication**.

> **Example 3:** What is the total cost of 231 meals that cost £34 each?

Partition first: 34 × 231 = (30 + 4) × (200 + 30 + 1)

Using the grid method:

×	200	30	1
30	6 000	900	30
4	800	120	4
=	6 800	1 020	34

```
  6 800
  1 020
     34 +
 £7 854
```

> **Tip**
>
> Multiply the number at the top of the column by the number at the start of each row, then add the results.

Answer: £7 854

5   You can use **repeated subtraction** for **long division**.

> **Example 4:** Buses that seat 36 people are to be used to transport 1 168 students. How many buses will be needed?

First work out some of the *multiples* of 36.

Subtract multiples of 36 from 1 168.

```
 1 168
  720  – 20 buses
  448
  360  – 10 buses
   88
   72  – 2 buses
   16
```

An extra bus is needed for the 16 students 'left over'.

Total number of buses = 20 + 10 + 2 + 1 = 33

Answer: 33

> **Test tip**
>
> Check your calculation by estimating:
> $35 \times 200 = 7\,000$

> **Tip**
>
> $1 \times 36 = 36$
> $2 \times 36 = 72$
> $10 \times 36 = 360$
> $20 \times 36 = 720$

▶▶ Now try it!

Try out each of the tips in these questions.

1. A man's shopping bill is £15.37. How much change will he receive from a £20 note?

   _____

2. A shopkeeper buys 4 000 England flags. On the first day he sells 437. How many flags are left?

   _____

3. **a** Four friends share a lottery win of £538. How much money do they each receive?

   _____

   b Convert 425 miles to kilometres. (Use 5 miles is approximately 8 km.)

   _____

4. Three hundred and fifty-two biology students go on a field trip that costs £23 each. What is the total cost?

   _____

5. Buses that hold 28 people are to be used to transport 1 432 students. How many buses will be needed?

   _____

▷ An integer is a _____ _____.

▷ The value of each digit in a number depends on its position in the number, its _____ _____.

▷ A _____ is one thousand million: 1 000 000 000 or 10^9.

▷ To round a number:

   ▷ Count along to the last digit that is needed.

   ▷ If the next digit is 5, 6, 7, 8 or 9, _____ the last digit up.

   ▷ If the next digit is 0, 1, 2, 3 or 4, _____ the last digit.

▷ To find the difference between two numbers:

   ▷ If the signs are the same, _____ the numbers.

   ▷ If the signs are different, _____ the numbers.

▷ A loss or overdraft is a _____ amount of money. A profit or credit is a _____ amount of money.

▷ The _____ of a number are the numbers that will divide into it exactly.

▷ A _____ number has exactly two factors: itself and 1.

▷ A product is the result of a _____.

▷ A _____ of a number can be divided exactly by that number.

▷ You _____ by rounding to 1 s.f.

▷ You can use an inverse calculation to _____ answers.

▷ To divide by 4, divide by ____ then divide by ____ again. To divide by 5, first multiply by ____ then divide by ____.

Now try it!

1. A company makes a profit of £653 172.

   What is this figure to the nearest £100 000?

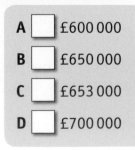

A ☐ £600 000

B ☐ £650 000

C ☐ £653 000

D ☐ £700 000

2. The attendance at a football match was 6 500 to the nearest 100.

   What is the smallest possible attendance?

   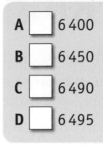

   A ☐ 6 400

   B ☐ 6 450

   C ☐ 6 490

   D ☐ 6 495

3. After a shopkeeper cleans his freezer its temperature is 7°C. The temperature should be −16°C before he puts his frozen food back in.

   By how many degrees must the temperature fall?

   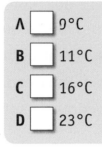

   A ☐ 9°C

   B ☐ 11°C

   C ☐ 16°C

   D ☐ 23°C

4. Some students organise a leavers' ball. The cost of the hall is £200 and the buffet is £15 per person.

   If there are 100 people, which of these calculations would you use to find out how much each would pay?

   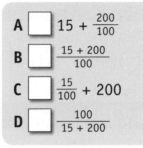

   A ☐ $15 + \frac{200}{100}$

   B ☐ $\frac{15 + 200}{100}$

   C ☐ $\frac{15}{100} + 200$

   D ☐ $\frac{100}{15 + 200}$

5. A man buys 13 T-shirts that cost £9.86 each. He calculates the total cost in four ways.

   Which of the given estimates is closest to the actual total?

   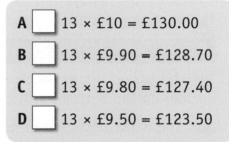

   A ☐ 13 × £10 = £130.00

   B ☐ 13 × £9.90 = £128.70

   C ☐ 13 × £9.80 = £127.40

   D ☐ 13 × £9.50 = £123.50

6. A coach company uses 53-seater coaches to transport passengers between Heathrow and Gatwick airports.

   How many coaches would be needed to transport 4 862 passengers?

   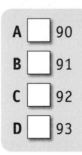

   A ☐ 90

   B ☐ 91

   C ☐ 92

   D ☐ 93

7. In one week a shopkeeper sold 451 DVD players for £36 each.

   What was the total amount of money the shopkeeper received for the DVD players?

   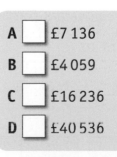

   A ☐ £7 136

   B ☐ £4 059

   C ☐ £16 236

   D ☐ £40 536

B Working with fractions

You should already know how to:

✔ read, write, order and compare common fractions and mixed numbers

✔ find parts of quantities or measurements.

By the end of this section you will know how to:

▷▷ find fractions of quantities

▷▷ express one number as a fraction of another

▷▷ use fractions to add and subtract amounts

▷▷ use fractions to solve practical problems.

1 Types of fraction

First read this ...

A **fraction** is a way of expressing a part of a whole.

The fraction $\frac{3}{4}$ means 3 parts out of 4.

The number on the top, 3, is called the **numerator**, the number on the bottom, 4, is called the **denominator**.

▷ You write a fraction in its *lowest terms* by *cancelling* any *common factors*.

In $\frac{14}{21}$ the numerator and denominator have a common factor of 7. You can divide 'top' and 'bottom' by 7:

$$\frac{14}{21} \xrightarrow[\div 7]{\div 7} = \frac{2}{3}$$

$\frac{14}{21}$ and $\frac{2}{3}$ are **equivalent fractions**.

You can find equivalent fractions by multiplying:

$\frac{3}{4}$ is equivalent to $\frac{6}{8}$

$$\frac{3}{4} \xrightarrow[\times 2]{\times 2} = \frac{6}{8}$$

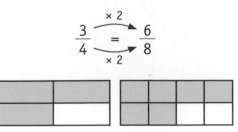

> **Remember**
>
> $\frac{1}{2}$ is bigger than $\frac{1}{3}$ which is bigger than $\frac{1}{4}$.
>
>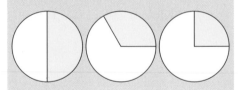

▷ In an **improper** fraction the numerator is bigger than the denominator.

You can write an improper fraction as a *mixed number*:

$$\frac{8}{5} = \frac{5}{5} \quad + \quad \frac{3}{5} = 1\frac{3}{5}$$

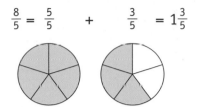

Remember

A mixed number has a whole number part and a fraction part.

You can change mixed numbers to improper fractions.

Example: Change $2\frac{7}{8}$ to an improper fraction.

Because the denominator of the fraction is 8 you need to change the mixed number to eighths.

One whole is $\frac{8}{8}$, so two wholes is $\frac{8}{8} + \frac{8}{8} = \frac{16}{8}$.

This means that $2\frac{7}{8} = \frac{8}{8} \quad + \quad \frac{8}{8} \quad + \quad \frac{7}{8} = \frac{23}{8}$.

Answer: $\frac{23}{8}$

Tip

A quick way of working this out is 2 × 8 + 7 = 23.

▶▶ Now try it!

1. Write these as fractions in their lowest terms.

    a $\frac{12}{16}$ b $\frac{15}{20}$ c $\frac{22}{25}$ d $\frac{81}{108}$

    _____   _____   _____   _____

2. Write these improper fractions as mixed numbers.

    a $\frac{16}{6}$ b $\frac{31}{7}$ c $\frac{21}{8}$ d $\frac{61}{9}$

    _____   _____   _____   _____

3. Write these mixed numbers as improper fractions.

    a $1\frac{5}{6}$ b $2\frac{3}{5}$ c $3\frac{5}{7}$ d $4\frac{3}{10}$

    _____   _____   _____   _____

First read this ...

▷ To find $\frac{1}{5}$ of a quantity, **divide** by 5.

▷ To find $\frac{2}{5}$ of a quantity, **divide** by 5, then **multiply** by 2.

Example 1: $\frac{3}{25}$ of the money spent on the National Lottery is paid to the Treasury in duty.
In a year when £5 billion is recorded in sales, how much money will be paid to the Treasury?

To find $\frac{1}{25}$ divide by 25.

To find $\frac{3}{25}$ multiply this answer by 3.

1 billion is 1 000 000 000 = 100 × 10 000 000

There are four 25s in every 100.

So $\frac{1\,000\,000\,000}{25}$ = 4 × 10 000 000 = 40 000 000

Then $\frac{3}{25}$ = 3 × 40 000 000 = £120 000 000

Answer: £120 million

Example 2: Out of 192 students, $\frac{5}{16}$ own a dog. $\frac{2}{3}$ of these students also own a cat. How many of these students own a dog and a cat?

You have to tackle this question in two stages.

To find out how many students own a dog, find $\frac{5}{16}$ of 192.

To find $\frac{5}{16}$, divide by 16 then multiply by 5.

You can work out $\frac{192}{16}$ by cancelling common factors.

$$\frac{192}{16} \xrightarrow[\div 2]{\div 2} = \frac{96}{8} \xrightarrow[\div 2]{\div 2} = \frac{48}{4} \xrightarrow[\div 2]{\div 2} = \frac{24}{2} = 12$$

$\frac{1}{16}$ of 192 is 12, so $\frac{5}{16}$ of 192 is 5 × 12 = 60.

So 60 students own a dog.

$\frac{2}{3}$ of these also own a cat.

You need to find $\frac{2}{3}$ of 60.

$\frac{1}{3}$ of 60 is $\frac{60}{3}$ = 20, so $\frac{2}{3}$ of 60 is 2 × 20 = 40.

Answer: 40 students own a dog and a cat.

Tip

When both numbers are even, then they must have a common factor of 2.

▶▶ *Now try it!*

1. 54 000 people attended a football match. $\frac{3}{8}$ of those who attended were children. How many children attended the football match?

   _____

   _____

2. In a business employing 1 080 people, $\frac{5}{12}$ of the employees are under 25. How many of the employees are under 25?

   _____

   _____

3. 1 250 people went to the local cinema on a Saturday night. Of these people, $\frac{2}{5}$ paid the student rate of £7.50 and the remainder paid the full adult rate of £10. What was the total amount of money paid to the cinema that night?

   _____

   _____

4. When 72 students sat the driving test theory exam, $\frac{5}{6}$ of them passed. Of these, $\frac{4}{5}$ went on to pass the driving test practical. How many of these students passed both the theory and the practical driving test exams?

   _____

   _____

Tip
First find the number of students who passed the exam.

5. A man earns £1 200 a month. He spends $\frac{3}{4}$ of his earnings on food and accommodation and saves $\frac{1}{5}$ of the rest. How much money does he save each month?

   _____

   _____

6. In a street with 420 houses, $\frac{5}{6}$ of the houses are owned by the occupiers, and $\frac{1}{10}$ of the rest are rented. How many houses in the street are rented?

   _____

   _____

First read this ...

▷ One number as a fraction of another number is:

$$\frac{\text{first number}}{\text{second number}}$$

Example 1: Express 8 as a fraction of 12.

8 as a fraction of 12 is $\frac{8}{12}$.

$$\frac{8}{12} \xrightarrow[\div 4]{\div 4} = \frac{2}{3}$$

Answer: $\frac{2}{3}$

To express one quantity as a fraction of another, the quantities must be in the same units.

Example 2: Express 60 g as a fraction of 1 kg.

Write the quantities in the same units.

$$\frac{60}{1\,000} \xrightarrow[\div 10]{\div 10} = \frac{6}{100} \xrightarrow[\div 2]{\div 2} = \frac{3}{50}$$

Answer: $\frac{3}{50}$

You can work out a fraction increase or decrease.

Find the actual increase or decrease first.

Example 3: On Monday 200 students used the college canteen. On Tuesday, 350 students used the canteen. By what fraction did the number of students using the canteen increase?

The actual increase in the number of students using the canteen on Tuesday is 350 – 200 = 150.

You express this as a fraction of the number of students using the canteen on Monday.

$$\frac{150}{200} \xrightarrow[\div 10]{\div 10} = \frac{15}{20} \xrightarrow[\div 5]{\div 5} = \frac{3}{4}$$

Answer: $\frac{3}{4}$

You can round numbers to find an **approximate fraction**.

Example 4: A college has a total of 1 060 students. 220 of them are studying mathematics. Approximately what fraction of the college students are studying mathematics?

The *exact* fraction is $\frac{220}{1060}$.

Writing both top and bottom correct to 1 significant figure gives:

$$\frac{200}{1\,000} \xrightarrow[\div\,10]{\div\,10} = \frac{2}{10} \xrightarrow[\div\,2]{\div\,2} = \frac{1}{5}$$

Answer: $\frac{1}{5}$

Test tip

Fraction questions like these always appear in the test.

▶▶ *Now try it!*

1. In a class of 30 students, 21 are girls.
    What fraction of the class are girls?

    _____

2. In a car park of 120 cars, 45 are made in Europe and the rest are made in Japan.
    What fraction of the cars are made in Japan?

    _____

3. Express 54 mm as a fraction of 20 cm in its simplest form.

    _____

Remember

1 cm = 10 mm

4. Sales at a clothes shop in January totalled £2 250.
    In February the sales totalled £750.
    By what fraction did the sales decrease in February?

    _____

5. In a survey, 120 students were asked how long they spent using a computer in one week.
    The results are shown below.

Number of hours	0–5	6–10	11–15	16+
Number of students	22	57	35	6

    What fraction of the students spent 10 or fewer hours using a computer in one week?

    _____

First read this ...

You use fractions when working with *time*.

▷ You can only add or subtract fractions with the same denominator.

If the denominators are different, you need to express them as equivalent fractions.

Example 1: Work out $\frac{1}{3} + \frac{3}{5}$.

Find the smallest number that both of the denominators will divide into.

The LCM of 3 and 5 is 15.

Change $\frac{1}{3}$ and $\frac{3}{5}$ to equivalent fractions with a denominator of 15.

$$\frac{1}{3} \xrightarrow[\times 5]{\times 5} \frac{5}{15} \quad \text{and} \quad \frac{3}{5} \xrightarrow[\times 3]{\times 3} \frac{9}{15}$$

$$\frac{5}{15} + \frac{9}{15} = \frac{14}{15}$$

Answer: $\frac{14}{15}$

Remember

The LCM (**lowest common multiple**) is the smallest number that two numbers will both divide into.

Tip

If the denominators do not have a common factor, you can find their LCM by multiplying the denominators together.

Example 2: Evaluate $1\frac{5}{12} + 2\frac{7}{8}$.

First add the whole numbers: $1 + 2 = 3$

Now add the fractions: $\frac{5}{12} + \frac{7}{8}$

The LCM of 12 and 8 is 24.

$$\frac{5}{12} \xrightarrow[\times 2]{\times 2} \frac{10}{24} \quad \text{and} \quad \frac{7}{8} \xrightarrow[\times 3]{\times 3} \frac{21}{24}$$

$$\frac{10}{24} + \frac{21}{24} = \frac{31}{24} = \frac{24}{24} + \frac{7}{24} = 1\frac{7}{24}$$

$$3 + 1\frac{7}{24} = 4\frac{7}{24}$$

Answer: $4\frac{7}{24}$

Example 3: Work out $\frac{7}{8} - \frac{4}{5}$.

The method is similar to addition.

The LCM of 8 and 5 is 40.

$$\frac{7}{8} \xrightarrow[\times 5]{\times 5} \frac{35}{40} \quad \text{and} \quad \frac{4}{5} \xrightarrow[\times 8]{\times 8} \frac{32}{40}$$

$$\frac{35}{40} - \frac{32}{40} = \frac{3}{40}$$

Answer: $\frac{3}{40}$

Example 4: Evaluate $3\frac{1}{6} - 1\frac{2}{3}$.

First subtract the whole numbers: $3 - 1 = 2$

Then work out $\frac{1}{6} - \frac{2}{3}$.

The LCM of 6 and 3 is 6.

$\frac{1}{6} - \frac{2}{3}$ becomes $\frac{1}{6} - \frac{4}{6} = -\frac{3}{6}$

$-\frac{3}{6} \xrightarrow[\div 3]{\div 3} -\frac{1}{2}$ in its lowest terms.

The answer is: $2 - \frac{1}{2} = 1\frac{1}{2}$

Answer: $1\frac{1}{2}$

Test tip

Questions involving fractions may ask you to 'work out', 'calculate' or 'evaluate'.

▶▶ *Now try it!*

1. Three TV programmes last for $1\frac{1}{2}$ hours, $\frac{3}{4}$ hour and $1\frac{3}{4}$ hours. If you watch them all, how long would this take?

   _____

   _____

2. A girl walks to the shops. It takes her $\frac{1}{2}$ hour to get there, she shops for $3\frac{1}{4}$ hours and it takes her $\frac{3}{4}$ hour to get back. How long did the shopping trip take?

   _____

   _____

3. A boy cycles to his friend's house. It takes him $1\frac{3}{4}$ hours to get there and $2\frac{1}{4}$ hours to cycle back.
   How much longer did it take him to cycle back from his friend's house?

   _____

   _____

Test tip

Read the question carefully. To find out how much longer, or shorter, you count on or subtract.
It can help to sketch a number line:

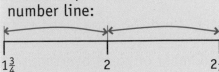

$1\frac{3}{4}$ 2 $2\frac{1}{4}$

4. A film lasts for $3\frac{3}{4}$ hours. An edited version of the film lasts for $2\frac{1}{2}$ hours. How much shorter is the edited film than the original version?

   _____

   _____

5 Using fractions to solve problems

First read this ...

You will often need to multiply or divide by a fraction.

Typical test questions involve salaries, distances and time.

▷ When dividing by a fraction, multiply top and bottom to make the denominator a **whole number**.

Example 1: A car has an average fuel consumption of $50\frac{1}{2}$ miles per gallon.
How many gallons of fuel would be needed for a journey of 202 miles?

Every $50\frac{1}{2}$ miles requires 1 gallon of fuel.

You need to find how many lots of $50\frac{1}{2}$ there are in 202.

$$\frac{202}{50\frac{1}{2}} \overset{\times 2}{\underset{\times 2}{=}} \frac{404}{101}$$

Multiplying both numbers by 2 to get rid of the fraction on the bottom.

$\frac{404}{101} = 4$ gallons

Answer: 4 gallons

▷ To multiply by a mixed number, partition it into a whole number and a fraction.

Example 2: A barman is paid £4.40 per hour for a 40-hour week and then at $1\frac{1}{2}$ times that rate for any extra hours he works overtime.
How much overtime pay is he paid on a week when he works 48 hours?

Work out the overtime rate of pay as follows:

$$£4.40 \times 1\frac{1}{2} = £4.40 \times (1 + \frac{1}{2})$$
$$= (£4.40 \times 1) + (£4.40 \times \frac{1}{2})$$
$$= £4.40 + £2.20$$
$$= £6.60$$

Number of hours overtime = 48 − 40 = 8 hours

Overtime pay = 8 × £6.60
$$= 8 \times (£6 + £0.60)$$
$$= £48 + £4.80$$
$$= £52.80$$

Answer: £52.80

> **Tip**
>
> $£4.40 \times \frac{1}{2} = \frac{£4.40}{2}$
> $= £2.20$

> **Test tip**
>
> Read the question carefully. You only want to know the **overtime** pay.

▶▶ *Now try it!*

1. On a sponsored walk a boy completes $3\frac{1}{2}$ miles.
    He was sponsored for £24 per mile.
    How much money will he collect?

    _____

    _____

2. A waitress's basic pay is £5.60 per hour. She is paid $1\frac{1}{4}$
    times the basic rate for any overtime she does.
    How much overtime pay does she receive in a week when
    she does 12 hours overtime?

    _____

    _____

3. A mortgage company offers to loan $2\frac{1}{2}$ times the joint
    annual income for a couple buying a house. Simon earns
    £20 000 a year and Claire earns £18 000 a year.
    How much can the couple borrow, based on their joint
    income?

    _____

    _____

4. A girl cycled 20 miles in $1\frac{1}{4}$ hours.
    What is her average speed, in miles per hour?

    _____

    _____

> **Remember**
>
> $speed = \dfrac{distance}{time}$

5. A shop recommends you buy $2\frac{1}{2}$ times the width of a
    window when buying net curtain. What width of net curtain
    would a man buy for a window which is 250 cm wide?

    _____

    _____

6. A café owner wants to buy 30 litres of lemonade. The
    lemonade is sold in $1\frac{1}{2}$ litre bottles. How many bottles of
    lemonade does he need to buy?

    _____

    _____

7. A fish tank holds 36 litres of water. It is filled up using a
    container which holds $4\frac{1}{2}$ litres of water. How many times
    does the container need to be filled with water and then
    emptied into the tank to completely fill the fish tank?

    _____

    _____

First complete this ...

▷ You write a fraction in its lowest terms by
_____ any common factors.

▷ In an _____ fraction the numerator is bigger
than the denominator.

▷ To find $\frac{1}{5}$ of a quantity, _____ by 5.

▷ To find $\frac{2}{5}$ of a quantity, _____ by 5, then
_____ by 2.

▷ One number as a fraction of another number is:
$$\frac{\text{_____ number}}{\text{_____ number}}$$

▷ You can only add or subtract fractions with the same
_____.

▷ When dividing by a fraction, multiply top and bottom to
make the denominator a _____ _____.

▷ To multiply by a mixed number, partition it into a whole
number and a _____.

Test tip

Before you can express one
quantity as a fraction of
another, you must write them
in the *same units*.

Now try it!

1. The total receipts for a football club match in one particular
    week were £640 000. The club spends $\frac{3}{8}$ of its income on
    salaries.

    How much of the week's receipts was spent on salaries?

    A ☐ £80 000

    B ☐ £70 000

    C ☐ £240 000

    D ☐ £210 000

2. A boy gets £10 a week in pocket money. He also receives £8
    a week for delivering newspapers.

    What fraction of his total income is the money he receives
    for delivering newspapers?

    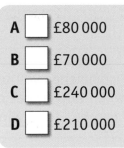

    A ☐ $\frac{1}{9}$

    B ☐ $\frac{4}{5}$

    C ☐ $\frac{4}{9}$

    D ☐ $\frac{5}{9}$

3. It takes a girl $1\frac{3}{4}$ hours to travel to the Trafford centre in
    Manchester. She spends $2\frac{1}{2}$ hours shopping and it takes
    her $1\frac{1}{4}$ hours to get home.

    How long does she take in total?

    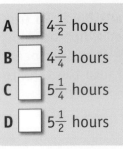

    A ☐ $4\frac{1}{2}$ hours

    B ☐ $4\frac{3}{4}$ hours

    C ☐ $5\frac{1}{4}$ hours

    D ☐ $5\frac{1}{2}$ hours

4. A car travels an average of $45\frac{1}{2}$ miles per gallon.
    The petrol tank holds 9 gallons of petrol when full.

    How many miles, on average, could the car travel with a full tank of petrol?

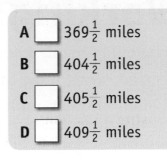

A ☐ $369\frac{1}{2}$ miles

B ☐ $404\frac{1}{2}$ miles

C ☐ $405\frac{1}{2}$ miles

D ☐ $409\frac{1}{2}$ miles

5. A dressmaker buys material that is 160 inches wide.
    1 inch is approximately $2\frac{1}{2}$ centimetres.

    What is the width of the material, in centimetres?

A ☐ 64 cm

B ☐ 70 cm

C ☐ 328 cm

D ☐ 400 cm

6. The price of a dress is reduced from £35 to £25 in a sale.

    What calculation would you do to find the decrease in price as a fraction of the original price?

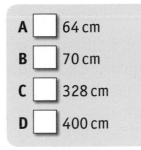

A ☐ $\frac{35 - 25}{25}$

B ☐ $\frac{35 - 25}{35}$

C ☐ $\frac{25}{35 - 25}$

D ☐ $\frac{35}{35 - 25}$

7. There are 90 cars in a car park. $\frac{2}{5}$ of these cars are red.
    $\frac{1}{3}$ of the red cars have three doors.

    How many cars in the car park are red with three doors?

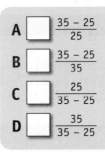

A ☐ 6 cars

B ☐ 10 cars

C ☐ 12 cars

D ☐ 15 cars

8. In a survey of 252 students, 147 of them had their own iPod.

    Approximately what fraction of the students had their own iPod?

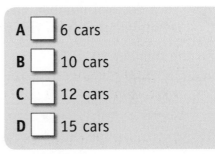

A ☐ $\frac{3}{8}$

B ☐ $\frac{3}{5}$

C ☐ $\frac{2}{5}$

D ☐ $\frac{5}{8}$

9. There were 5 261 people in a village. At an election 1 933 voted Conservative.

    Approximately what fraction of the people in the village voted Conservative?

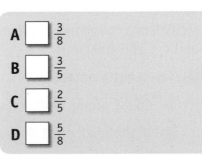

A ☐ $\frac{1}{5}$

B ☐ $\frac{1}{3}$

C ☐ $\frac{2}{5}$

D ☐ $\frac{2}{3}$

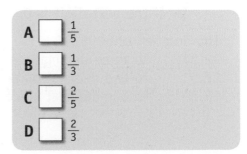

C Working with decimals

You should already know how to:

✔ read, write, order and compare decimals

✔ add, subtract, multiply and divide decimals with up to 2 decimal places

✔ multiply and divide decimals by 10 and 100.

By the end of this section you will know how to:

▷ order, approximate and compare decimals

▷ calculate with decimals with up to 3 decimal places

▷ calculate and estimate amounts of money and convert between currencies.

---

1 Decimal numbers

First read this ...

▷ In a decimal number, the decimal point separates the whole number from the part that is less than 1.

In the number 10.357:

Tens	Units	•	Tenths	Hundredths	Thousandths
1	0	•	3	5	7

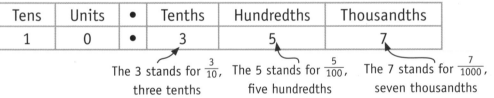

The 3 stands for $\frac{3}{10}$, three tenths

The 5 stands for $\frac{5}{100}$, five hundredths

The 7 stands for $\frac{7}{1000}$, seven thousandths

Calculations involving decimals follow the rules for whole numbers and fractions.

▷ To round a number:

　▷ Count along to the last digit that is needed.

　▷ If the next digit is 5, 6, 7, 8 or 9, round the last digit up.

　▷ If the next digit is 0, 1, 2, 3 or 4, leave the last digit.

The number 12.5095 is:
12.510　to three decimal places
12.51　to two decimal places
12.5　to one decimal place.

> **Test tip**
>
> Answers to money calculations in pounds should be written correct to the nearest penny (two decimal places).

Example 1: A plumber cuts three lengths of pipe measuring 1.102 m, 1.204 m and 0.426 m. What is the total length of pipe he uses?

Line up the numbers using the decimal points.

1	.	1	0	2
1	.	2	0	4
0	.	4	2	6
2	.	7	¹3	2

Answer: 2.732 m

Example 2: One yard is equal to 3 feet. One foot is equal to 12 inches. 1 inch is approximately equal to 2.54 cm. What is one yard, in centimetres?

The calculation is:

×	2	0.5	0.04
30	60	15	1.2
6	12	3	0.24
=	72	18	1.44

$3 \times 12 \times 2.54$
$= 36 \times 2.54$
$= (30 + 6) \times (2 + 0.5 + 0.04)$
$= 72 + 18 + 1.44 = 91.44$

Answer: 91.44 cm

▶▶ Now try it!

1. 1 inch is approximately 2.5 centimetres. Approximately how long is 18 inches in centimetres?

2. One petrol station sells petrol for £0.929 per litre, another sells petrol for £0.948 per litre.

   a What is the difference in the price per litre?

   b How much could a driver save by buying 20 litres at the lower price?

3. A boy weighs 7 stones 12 pounds. 14 pounds = 1 stone and 1 kg = 2.2 pounds. How much does the boy weigh, in kilograms?

4. A car's petrol tank holds 12 gallons of petrol when full. 1 gallon is approximately 4.55 litres. What is 12 gallons, in litres?

2 Calculating with money

First read this ...

Money problems often involve decimal calculations.

Example 1: A company charges a fixed cost of £7 for specially designed cards, plus a printing charge of 5p for each card.
a How much will they charge for an order of 120 cards?
b How many cards would you get for £20?

The final price is in pounds, so change the pence to pounds.
5p = £0.05

a The cost for the cards is 120 × 0.05
$$= 12 \times 0.5$$
$$= 12 \times \frac{1}{2} = £6$$

So the total cost is £7 + £6 = £13

Answer: £13

b To find the printing charge, subtract the fixed cost of £7.

The printing charge is £20 – £7 = £13

Each card costs 5p to print, so work out how many 5ps there are in £13:

$$\frac{13}{0.05} \xrightarrow[\times 100]{\times 100} = \frac{1300}{5} \xrightarrow[\div 5]{\div 5} = \frac{260}{1} = 260$$

Answer: 260 cards

Example 2: £1 = $1.85
a Use the above exchange rate to change £250 to dollars.
b What calculation would you do to check your answer?

a Every £1 is worth $1.85.
There will be more dollars than pounds, so multiply:

$$250 \times 1.85 = (250 \times 1) + (250 \times 0.8) + (250 \times 0.05)$$
$$= 250 + 200 + 12.50$$
$$= 462.50$$

Answer: $462.50

b The calculation is:

£250 → [× 1.85] → $462.50

To check the calculation, start from $462.50 and work backwards, doing the inverse operation.

£250 ← [÷ 1.85] ← $462.50

Answer: $\frac{\$462.50}{1.85} = £250$

Test tip

If the final answer is in pounds, change any pence to pounds.

Tip

120 × 0.05 = 12 × 10 × 0.05
= 12 × 0.5

Tip

To change from pounds to euros, *multiply* by 1.45.
To change from pounds to dollars, *multiply* by 1.85.

Remember

+ is the inverse of –
× is the inverse of ÷

▶▶ *Now try it!*

1. The cost of hiring a carpet cleaner is £15 basic charge plus £12.50 per day. What is the cost of hiring a carpet cleaner for four days?

_____

2. A man earns a basic rate of £12.20 per hour for a 35-hour week. For each hour worked over 35 hours he earns 1.25 times the basic rate. How much does the man earn in a week when he works 40 hours?

_____

3. A T-shirt company sells personalised T-shirts with names printed on them. The company charges £10.99 for each T-shirt plus 8p for each letter printed on it. How much will it cost to have the name 'Alexander' printed on a T-shirt?

_____

4. A children's entertainer charges a fixed fee of £60 plus £8.50 per hour to attend a party. How much does she charge to attend a party for 3.5 hours?

_____

5. A woman is buying an outfit for a wedding. She spends £125.99 on a dress, £56 on shoes and £70.50 on a hat. Round the prices to the nearest pound to estimate the total cost of her outfit.

_____

6. A girl receives 464 euros in exchange for £320. The exchange rate is £1 = 1.45 euros. What calculation would you do to check this is correct?

_____

7. A car is priced at 12 000 euros. If £3 = 5 euros, what is the price of the car, in pounds?

_____

_____

> **Test tip**
>
> Check your answer is sensible. £3 = 5 euros, so you need fewer pounds than euros.

8. £1 = $1.85. Use this rate to change £280 to dollars.

_____

_____

First complete this ...

▷ In a decimal number, the _____ _____ separates the whole number from the part that is less than 1.

▷ To round a number:

  ▷ Count along to the last digit that is needed.

  ▷ If the next digit is 5, 6, 7, 8 or 9, _____ the last digit up.

  ▷ If the next digit is 0, 1, 2, 3 or 4, _____ the last digit.

▷ Answers to money calculations in pounds should be written correct to the nearest penny (_____ decimal places).

Test tip

It helps to identify which of the answers is *not* a solution to the problem. You can do this by estimation or using the tips given in this section.

Now try it!

1. A car travels at 60 mph. 1 mile is roughly 1.6 km.

   What is the speed in km per hour?

   A ☐ 37 km per hour

   B ☐ 38 km per hour

   C ☐ 90 km per hour

   D ☐ 96 km per hour

2. A garage records the carbon monoxide emissions of two cars. One emits 0.341 g/km and the other emits 1.154 g/km.

   What is the difference in the emissions, to the nearest tenth of a g/km?

   A ☐ 0.7 g/km

   B ☐ 0.8 g/km

   C ☐ 0.9 g/km

   D ☐ 1.0 g/km

3. The exchange rate on a particular day is 1 euro = 69.2 pence.

   How would you calculate the value of £150 in euros?

   A ☐ $\dfrac{69.2}{150 \times 100}$

   B ☐ $\dfrac{150}{69.2 \times 100}$

   C ☐ $\dfrac{69.2 \times 100}{150}$

   D ☐ $\dfrac{150 \times 100}{69.2}$

4. A dog weighs 26 pounds. 1 kg is approximately 2.2 pounds.

How much does the dog weigh, in kilograms, to the nearest kilogram?

A ☐ 12 kg

B ☐ 13 kg

C ☐ 58 kg

D ☐ 57 kg

5. A garage charges £32.50 per hour for labour plus the cost of parts. The repairs to a woman's car take 3.2 hours and the parts cost £115.70. Her total bill is £219.70.

Which one of these calculations checks the total bill?

A ☐ $\dfrac{219.7 \quad 115.7}{32.5} = 3.2$

B ☐ $\dfrac{219.7}{32.5} - 115.7 = 3.2$

C ☐ $\dfrac{219.7 - 32.5}{3.2} = 115.7$

D ☐ $\dfrac{219.7 - 32.5}{115.7} = 3.2$

6. A boy is buying Christmas presents. He buys a CD for £9.50, a pair of gloves for £12.99, a book for £5.75 and a game for £8.20.

Round the prices to the nearest pound to estimate the total.

A ☐ £35

B ☐ £36

C ☐ £37

D ☐ £38

7. On a particular day the exchange rate between pounds and dollars is £1 = $1.85 dollars.

How much is £400 worth, in dollars?

A ☐ $216

B ☐ $418.50

C ☐ $720

D ☐ $740

8. The diagram shows the work surface in a kitchen. The surface is to be covered with marble.

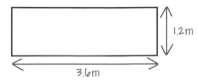

1.2 m

3.6 m

What is the area of the work surface?

A ☐ 3.6 m²

B ☐ 4.032 m²

C ☐ 4.32 m²

D ☐ 4.8 m²

9. An office manager is buying IT equipment. She buys three desktop PC base units at £487.64 each, two CRT monitors at £102.48 each and one LCD monitor at £186.85. She rounds the prices to the nearest pound to estimate the total.

What is the total?

A ☐ £1 367

B ☐ £1 851

C ☐ £1 855

D ☐ £1 857

D Working with percentages

You should already know how to:

✓ read, write, order and compare simple percentages

✓ understand simple percentage increase and decrease

✓ find simple percentage parts of quantities and measurements.

By the end of this section you will know how to:

▷▷ calculate percentage increase and decrease

▷▷ calculate using percentages in everyday contexts

▷▷ evaluate one number as an (approximate) percentage of another

▷▷ calculate percentage change.

1 Percentages

❚❚ First read this ...

▷ A percentage is a way of expressing a number as a proportion of 100.

For example, $30\% = \frac{30}{100} = \frac{3}{10}$.

Remember

$10\% = \frac{10}{100} = \frac{1}{10}$
To find 10%, divide by 10.
■ $5\% = 10\% \div 2$
■ $20\% = 10\% \times 2$

Example 1: Find 30% of 60.

10% of 60 is 6, so 30% of 60 is $3 \times 6 = 18$

Answer: 18

You can increase a quantity by a percentage.

▷ The original quantity is 100%. The increased quantity will be more than 100%.

Example 2: Increase 40 by 25%.

Test tip

Check your answer is more than the original amount

First find 25% of 40.

$$\frac{\overset{5}{\cancel{25}}}{\underset{2}{\cancel{10}\,\cancel{100}}} \times \frac{\overset{2}{\cancel{40}}}{1} = 10 \qquad \text{This is the amount it is increased by.}$$

$40 + 10 = 50$

Answer: 50

You can work out a percentage increase in a single calculation:

$$100\% + 25\% = 125\%$$

$$125\% \times 40 = \frac{125}{100} \times \frac{40}{1} = 50$$

You can decrease a quantity by a percentage.

▷ The original quantity is 100%. The decreased quantity will be less than 100%.

Example 3: Decrease 80 by 75%.

First find 75% of 80.

$$\frac{75}{100} \times \frac{80}{1} = 60 \qquad \text{This is the amount it is decreased by.}$$

$$80 - 60 = 20$$

Answer: 20

Tip

You can also find 25% mentally:

$25\% = \frac{1}{4}$

$\frac{1}{4}$ of 40 = 10

so 125% of 40 = 10 + 40 = 50

Tip

In a single calculation:

$100\% - 75\% = 25\%$

25% of 80 = 20

▶▶ *Now try it!*

Try out each of the above methods in these questions and decide which you like best.

1. Decrease 75 by 4%.

2. Increase 80 by 5%.

3. Increase 45 by 40%.

4. Decrease 400 by 1%.

5. Increase 250 by 20%.

6. Decrease 620 by 15%.

7. Decrease 180 by 2%.

8. Increase 5 by 30%.

2 Using percentages

First read this ...

Prices can be *increased* by a percentage, for example when VAT is added, or they can be *decreased*, for example in a sale.

Example 1: A clothes shop reduces its prices by 30% in a sale. What is the sale price of a dress that cost £50 before the sale?

Original price is 100%.

Sale price is 100% – 30% = 70%.

100% = £50
10% = £5

70% = 7 × 5 = £35

Answer: £35

Remember

When working with questions involving money, give your answers to *two* decimal places. For example, an answer of 3.5 means £3.50.

Example 2: A television costs £300 plus VAT at $17\frac{1}{2}$ %. What is the total price of the television, including VAT?

100% = £300
10% = £30
5% = £15

$2\frac{1}{2}$ % = £7.50   so $17\frac{1}{2}$ % = 30 + 15 + 7.50 = £52.50

Total cost of television = £300 + £52.50 = £352.50

Answer: £352.50

Remember

VAT is Value Added Tax.

▷ One number as a percentage of another is:
$\frac{\text{first number}}{\text{second number}} \times 100$

Example 3: Express 55p as a percentage of £11.

£11 = 1 100p

$\frac{55}{1100} \times \frac{100}{1} = 5$

Answer: 5%

Remember

To express one quantity as a percentage of another, you must write them in the same units.

Sometimes test questions ask for the *approximate* percentage.

Example 4: A company has 794 employees. In a survey, 157 said they travelled to work by motorbike. Approximately what percentage of the employees travel to work by motorbike?

Approximate 794 to 800 and 157 to 160 (8 is a factor of 16).

Now work out the fraction $\frac{160}{800}$ as a percentage.

$\frac{160}{800} \times \frac{100}{1} = 20$

Answer: 20%

▶▶ *Now try it!*

1. McDonut's reduce the price of their food by 20% in a sales promotion. A double burger usually costs £1.50. How much will it cost in the sales promotion?

2. A girl puts £200 into a savings account that has an interest rate of 4.5% AER. She leaves the money in the account. How much will she have in the account at the end of the year?

> **Tip**
>
> The AER is the Annual Equivalent Rate, used to help compare rates for savings.

3. The VAT on gas and electricity bills is 5%. How much VAT will be added to a monthly gas bill of £55?

4. A DVD player costs £120 before VAT of $17\frac{1}{2}$ % is added. What is the cost of the DVD player, including VAT?

5. Write 21 as a percentage of 70.

6. Express 54 mm as a percentage of 20 cm.

> **Tip**
>
> 10 mm = 1 cm

7. The price of a sandwich in a canteen has risen from £1.24 to £1.51. Express the increase in price as an approximate percentage of the original price.

8. In a car park of 1 200 cars, 423 were made in Europe and the rest were made in Japan. Approximately what percentage of the cars were made in Japan?

First read this ...

You find a percentage change using this formula:

▷ $$\text{percentage change} = \frac{\text{actual change}}{\text{original value}} \times 100$$

Example 1: In 2004, 640 million mobile phones were sold. In 2005, 720 million mobile phones were sold. What is the percentage increase in the number of mobile phones sold from 2004 to 2005?

For percentage increase the formula is:

$$\text{percentage increase} = \frac{\text{actual increase}}{\text{original value}} \times 100$$

Actual increase = 720 – 640 = 80 million

$$\text{Percentage increase} = \frac{\overset{10}{\cancel{80}}}{\underset{8}{\cancel{640}}_{64}} \times \frac{\overset{10}{\cancel{100}}}{1} = 12.5\%$$

Answer: 12.5%

Example 2: A shopkeeper buys 150 kg of bananas for £110 and sells them for 90 pence per kilogram. What is his percentage profit? Give your answer to one decimal place.

For percentage profit the formula is:

$$\text{percentage profit} = \frac{\text{actual profit}}{\text{original value}} \times 100$$

Cost price = £110

Selling price = (90 × 150) pence
= (90 × 100) + (90 × 50)
= 9 000 + 4 500
= 13 500 pence = £135

Actual profit = £135 – £110 = £25

$$\text{Percentage profit} = \frac{25}{\underset{11}{\cancel{110}}} \times \frac{\overset{10}{\cancel{100}}}{1}$$

$$= \frac{250}{11} = 250 \div 11$$

$$\begin{array}{r} 2\,2.\,7 \\ 11\overline{)25^30.^80} \end{array}$$

$$= 22.7\%$$

Answer: 22.7%

▶▶ *Now try it!*

1. In April, 1250 people visited an art exhibition. In May, 1675 people visited the art exhibition. What was the percentage increase in the number of visitors to the art exhibition between April and May?

   _____

   _____

2. A hockey club bought 150 sweatshirts for £1500. The same club sold the sweatshirts for £12.50 each. What was the percentage profit?

   _____

   _____

3. A man bought a car for £1500. He later sold it for £1200. What was his percentage loss?

   _____

   _____

4. A factory employed 360 workers. The number of workers decreased to 342. What was the percentage decrease in the number of workers?

   _____

   _____

5. In 2004, a large company makes a profit of £750000. In 2005 the company makes a profit of £1m. What is the percentage increase in the profit.

   _____

   _____

6. A clothes shop reduces the price of T-shirts from £2.50 to £2. What is the percentage discount?

   _____

   _____

7. A shopkeeper buys 100 umbrellas for £500. He sells the first 75 for £6 each and the rest for £4 each. What is his percentage profit?

   _____

   _____

First complete this ...

▷ A percentage is a way of expressing a number as a proportion of _____.

▷ To find 10%, divide by _____.

  ▷ 5% = 10% _____ 2

  ▷ 20% = 10% _____ 2

▷ The original quantity is _____.
The increased quantity will be _____ than 100%.
The decreased quantity will be _____ than 100%.

▷ One number as a percentage of another is:

$$\frac{_____ \text{ number}}{_____ \text{ number}} \times 100$$

▷ percentage change = $\dfrac{\text{actual change}}{_____ _____} \times 100$

Test tip

Read VAT questions carefully – do you want the VAT, or the price including VAT?

Test tip

The quantities must be in the same units.

Test tip

The word 'change' may be replaced by 'increase', 'decrease', 'profit' or 'loss'.

▶▶ Now try it!

1. 28% of the money spent on the National Lottery goes to good causes.

   How much money went to good causes in a year when £6 000 000 000 was spent on the National Lottery?

   A ☐ £1.68 million

   B ☐ £16.8 million

   C ☐ £168 million

   D ☐ £1 680 million

2. A shopkeeper changes his opening hours. He used to open from 9.00am to 5.00pm, but he now opens from 8.00am to 6.00pm.

   What is the percentage increase in the number of hours the shop is open?

   A ☐ 20%

   B ☐ 25%

   C ☐ 75%

   D ☐ 80%

3. A cleaner's basic rate of £8.60 per hour is increased by 3%.

   Which calculation gives the new basic rate per hour?

   A ☐ $£8.60 \times \frac{3}{100}$

   B ☐ $£8.60 + 3 \times 100$

   C ☐ $£\frac{3 \times 100}{8.60}$

   D ☐ $£\left(8.60 \times \frac{3}{100}\right) + 8.60$

4. A shopkeeper bought a television for £300 and sold it for £335.

    Which calculation gives the percentage profit?

    A $\frac{335-300}{300} \times 100$

    B $\frac{335-300}{335} \times 100$

    C $\frac{300}{335-300} \times 100$

    D $\frac{335}{335-300} \times 100$

5. In a survey, 25 students were asked how much time they had spent on revision and homework in one week. The results are shown in the table below.

Number of hours	Number of students
0 to less than 5	2
5 to less than 10	6
10 to less than 15	12
15 to less than 20	4
20 or more	1

    What percentage of the students spent between 10 and 15 hours on their homework?

    A 12%

    B 48%

    C 25%

    D 15%

6. In a sale, a carpet store reduces the price of its carpets by 40%. Before the sale, one particular carpet cost £20.50 per square metre.

    What is the sale price of this carpet per square metre?

    A £8.00

    B £8.20

    C £12

    D £12.30

7. In a survey of 500 shoppers in Oxford High Street, 137 of them had used the park-and-ride scheme to get to the city centre.

    Approximately what percentage is this?

    A 30%

    B 29%

    C 28%

    D 27%

8. A health-and-fitness club offers membership for £25 per month for 12 months, or £275 for the whole year.

    Which calculation gives the percentage saved by paying £275 for the year?

    A $\frac{25 \times 12 - 275}{275} \times 100$

    B $\frac{25 \times 12 - 275}{25 \times 12} \times 100$

    C $\frac{275}{25 \times 12 - 275} \times 100$

    D $\frac{25 \times 12}{25 \times 12 - 275} \times 100$

E Working with fractions, decimals and percentages

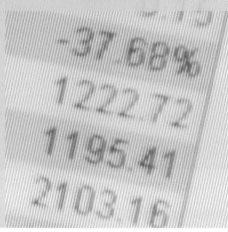

You should already know how to:

✔ recognise equivalencies between common fractions, percentages and decimals and use these to find part of whole-number quantities.

By the end of this section you will know how to:

▷▷ identify equivalences between fractions, decimals and percentages

▷▷ use fractions, decimals and percentages in practical problems to compare amounts.

1 Converting between forms

▌▌ *First read this ...*

▷ To convert a **fraction to a decimal**, *divide the numerator by the denominator.*

Example 1: Convert $\frac{1}{3}$ to a decimal.

$\frac{1}{3} = 1 \div 3$ which gives 0.3333333...

Answer: 0.3333333...

Tip

0.333333... is an example of a *recurring decimal*.
It can be written as $0.\dot{3}$.

You use **place value** to convert a decimal to a fraction.

Example 2: Convert 0.125 to a fraction.

$$0.125 = \frac{125}{1000} \xrightarrow{\div 5} = \frac{25}{200} \xrightarrow{\div 5} = \frac{5}{40} \xrightarrow{\div 5} = \frac{1}{8}$$

Answer: $\frac{1}{8}$

Remember

To write fractions in their *lowest terms, cancel* any common factors.

▷ To convert a **fraction or decimal to a percentage**, *multiply by 100.*

Example 3: Convert $\frac{5}{8}$ to a percentage.

$$_2\frac{5}{8} \times \frac{100^{25}}{1} = \frac{125}{2} = 62.5\%$$

Answer: 62.5%

Tip

Remember to simplify the multiplication by cancelling.

Example 4: Convert 0.462 to a percentage.

You need to work out 0.462 × 100 = 46.2.

Answer: 46.2%

Tip

Multiplying by 100 moves all the digits two places to the left.

42

▷ To convert a **percentage to a fraction or decimal**, *divide by 100*.

Example 5: Convert 65% to a fraction.

$65\% = \frac{65}{100} = \frac{13}{20}$

Answer: $\frac{13}{20}$

Example 6: Convert 2.5% to a decimal.

$2.5\% = \frac{2.5}{100} = 0.025$

Answer: 0.025

▷ Remember these equivalences:

Fraction	Decimal	Percentage	Fraction	Decimal	Percentage
$\frac{1}{10}$	0.1	10%	$\frac{1}{2}$	0.5	50%
$\frac{1}{4}$	0.25	25%	$\frac{2}{3}$	$0.\dot{6}$	$66.\dot{6}\%$ or $66\frac{2}{3}\%$
$\frac{1}{3}$	$0.\dot{3}$	$33.\dot{3}\%$ or $33\frac{1}{3}\%$	$\frac{3}{4}$	0.75	75%

Example 7: Four students estimate the profit they will make in organising the end-of-year ball. Their estimates are $\frac{1}{4}$, $\frac{1}{3}$, 35% and 0.2. Which is the largest of these estimates?

To compare the estimates, change them all to the same form. The easiest form is percentages.

$\frac{1}{4} \times 100 = 25\%$ $\frac{1}{3} \times 100 = 33\frac{1}{3}\%$

35% $0.2 \times 100 = 20\%$

The largest is 35%.

Answer: 35%

▶▶ Now try it!

1. Change each of these fractions to a decimal and a percentage.

   a $\frac{4}{5}$ _____   b $\frac{3}{20}$ _____

   c $\frac{7}{25}$ _____   d $\frac{7}{8}$ _____

2. Change each of these decimals to a percentage and a fraction.

   a 0.16 _____   b 0.32 _____

   c 0.08 _____   d 0.56 _____

3. Change each of these percentages to a decimal and a fraction.

   a 64% _____   b 24% _____

   c 45% _____   d 8.5% _____

First complete this ...

▷ To convert a fraction to a decimal, divide the _____ by the _____.

▷ To convert a fraction or decimal to a percentage, _____ by 100.

▷ To convert a percentage to a fraction or decimal, _____ by 100.

▷ Remember these equivalences:

Fraction	Decimal	Percentage
_____	0.1	10%
$\frac{1}{4}$	_____	25%
$\frac{1}{3}$	_____	33.$\dot{3}$% or $33\frac{1}{3}$%
$\frac{1}{2}$	0.5	_____
$\frac{2}{3}$	_____	66.$\dot{6}$% or $66\frac{2}{3}$%
_____	0.75	75%

Now try it!

1. A shopkeeper keeps a record of the different types of video she sells. About $\frac{5}{8}$ of the videos are 180 minutes long.

   What percentage is closest to $\frac{5}{8}$?

   A ☐ 16%
   B ☐ 58%
   C ☐ 63%
   D ☐ 85%

2. On average, only 8% of people who attend a local cinema buy membership.

   Which fraction is closest to 8%?

   A ☐ $\frac{8}{10}$
   B ☐ $\frac{8}{12}$
   C ☐ $\frac{1}{8}$
   D ☐ $\frac{1}{12}$

3. In a survey of 16 to 18-year-olds at FE colleges:
   - $\frac{2}{5}$ were studying economics
   - 2 in every 100 were studying physics
   - 22% were studying law
   - 2 in every ten were studying psychology

   According to the survey, what was the most common subject studied?

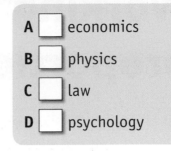

   A ☐ economics

   B ☐ physics

   C ☐ law

   D ☐ psychology

4. A survey of a sample of library users showed that $\frac{3}{8}$ were children.

   What is this fraction as a decimal?

   A ☐ 0.375

   B ☐ 0.380

   C ☐ 0.625

   D ☐ 0.830

5. Four friends estimate the amount of fat in their Indian take-away as $\frac{1}{5}$, 22%, 0.26 and $\frac{1}{4}$.

   Which is the highest estimate?

   A ☐ $\frac{1}{5}$

   B ☐ 22%

   C ☐ 0.26

   D ☐ $\frac{1}{4}$

6. Estimates for the number of vegetarians in a company are $\frac{1}{8}$, 10%, 0.08 and $\frac{1}{7}$.

   Which is the smallest estimate?

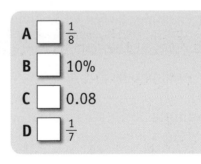

   A ☐ $\frac{1}{8}$

   B ☐ 10%

   C ☐ 0.08

   D ☐ $\frac{1}{7}$

7. $\frac{1}{6}$ of the people questioned in a survey said they did not vote in the last election.

   What percentage is closest to $\frac{1}{6}$?

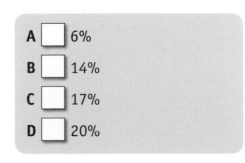

   A ☐ 6%

   B ☐ 14%

   C ☐ 17%

   D ☐ 20%

45

F Working with ratio and proportion

You should already know how to:

✔ work out simple ratio and direct proportion.

By the end of this section you will know how to:

▷▷ write a ratio in its simplest terms

▷▷ use direct proportion to scale quantities up or down

▷▷ use ratio in calculations

▷▷ work out dimensions from scale drawings.

1 Writing a ratio

First read this ...

▷ A **ratio** is a way of comparing two or more quantities.

The numbers are written with a colon between them.

▷ You usually write ratios in their simplest form.

For example, $8:6 = 4:3$, dividing both numbers by 2.

The order of the numbers in a ratio is important.

For example, $4:3$ is not the same as $3:4$.

Example 1: In a particular week, a total of 1 050 people visited a leisure centre. 675 were children and the rest were adults. What is the ratio of the number of children to the number of adults, in its simplest form?

If there are 675 children, then the number of adults is $1\,050 - 675 = 375$. The order of the ratio is important.

Number of children : number of adults = $675:375$

Dividing both numbers by 25 and then by 3:

$$\frac{675}{375} \xrightarrow[\div 25]{\div 25} \frac{27}{15} \xrightarrow[\div 3]{\div 3} \frac{9}{5}$$

Answer: $9:5$

Remember

Writing a ratio in its simplest form is like writing a fraction in its lowest terms: divide all the terms by any common factors.

Tip

Ratios do not have units. $2:5$ could mean 2 cm to 5 cm or 2 m to 5 m.

Tip

There are four 25s in every hundred so, for example, in 600 there will be $4 \times 6 = 24$.

Example 2: Write down the ratio of 45 minutes to 2 hours and simplify it.

Express the times in the same units by changing the hours to minutes. 2 hours = 2 × 60 = 120 minutes.

Now write the ratio without units:

45 : 120

Dividing both numbers by 5 and then by 3:

45 : 120
= 9 : 24
= 3 : 8

Answer: 3 : 8

Test tip

To compare units of measure, make sure they are *in the same units*.

▶▶ *Now try it!*

For each of these, find the ratio in its simplest form.

1. On a bus there are 24 seats upstairs and 27 seats downstairs. What is the ratio of the number of seats upstairs to the number of seats downstairs?

2. One morning a postman delivered 42 first-class letters and 48 second-class letters. What is the ratio of the number of first-class letters to the number of second-class letters?

3. The area of the Earth's surface is approximately equal to 510 000 000 km². Land covers approximately 150 000 000 km² and sea covers the rest of the surface. What is the approximate ratio of land to sea?

4. On a camp site there are 12 caravans, 15 tents and 27 cabins. What is the ratio of the number of caravans to the number of tents to the number of cabins?

5. In a business, it takes 55 minutes to deal with an internet order and 1 hour and 5 minutes to deal with a telephone order. What is the ratio of the time an internet order takes to the time a telephone order takes?

6. A small packet of crisps costs 35p. A family packet costs £2.45. What is the ratio of the cost of the smaller packet to the cost of the family packet?

Test tip

Make sure the quantities are in the same unit.

2 Scaling quantities up or down

First read this ...

When there is a ratio between quantities, they increase or decrease in the same **proportion**.

▷ You can use a ratio to scale quantities up or down. You multiply or divide each amount by the same number.

Example 1: A recipe for eight portions of shortbread takes:
• 150 g plain flour • 100 g butter • 50 g caster sugar
What quantities are needed for 12 portions?

The quantities need to stay in the same proportion. Find the ratio and multiply each term by the same number.

8 portions require 150 : 100 : 50.

4 (= 8 × $\frac{1}{2}$) portions will need half as much of each.

• 75 g plain flour • 50 g butter • 25 g caster sugar

12 (= 4 × 3) portions will need three times as much:

• 75 × 3 = 225 g plain flour • 50 × 3 = 150 g butter
• 25 × 3 = 75 g caster sugar

Answer: 225 g plain flour, 150 g butter, 75 g caster sugar

> **Tip**
>
> 150 : 100 : 50,
> 75 : 50 : 25 and
> 225 : 150 : 75
> are all equivalent ratios.

▶▶ Now try it!

1. It is estimated that swimming for 15 minutes will burn up 75 calories. Approximately how many calories would you burn up in a 45 minute swim?

   _____

2. A 75 centilitre carton of orange juice contains enough orange juice to fill six small glasses. How many small glasses will three one-litre cartons fill? 1 litre = 100 cl.

   _____

3. A recipe for a sponge cake providing eight portions takes:
   • 110 g butter • 110 g caster sugar
   • 110 g self-raising flour • 2 eggs

   a How much butter, caster sugar and self-raising flour are needed if 3 eggs are used in the recipe?

   _____

   b How many 250 g packs of butter are needed to make 140 portions of sponge cake?

   _____

3 Calculations with ratio

First read this ...

You can share a quantity in a given ratio.

▷ Think of a ratio as being made up of a number of parts:
3 : 2 is three parts to two parts, a total of five parts.

Example 1: Pink paint is made by mixing white paint with red paint in the ratio 3 : 2. A girl needs 10 litres of pink paint for her room, how much white paint does she need?

There are three parts of white paint for every two parts of red paint. This makes a total of 3 + 2 = 5 parts.

If 10 litres is split into 5 parts, then
5 parts = 10 litres means 1 part = 2 litres
3 parts of white = 3 × 2 = 6 litres

Answer: 6 litres

Tip

Check:
2 parts of red = 2 × 2 = 4 litres
6 + 4 = 10 litres.

Example 2: Mortar for laying bricks is made up of sand and cement in the ratio 7 : 3. If 140 kg of sand is used, how much mortar can be made?

Here 7 parts = 140 kg, so 1 part = 140 ÷ 7 = 20 kg

There is a total of 10 parts (7 parts sand + 3 parts cement)

So the total amount of mortar is 10 × 20 = 200 kg

Answer: 200 kg

Test tip

Questions often say 'share' or give a ratio and one quantity and ask for another quantity.

▷▷ Now try it!

1. A girl and a boy share the weekly rent on their flat in the ratio 5 : 4. The weekly rent is £90. How much does the girl pay per week?

   _____

2. Two gardeners share 132 kg of compost in the ratio 2 : 9. How much does each one get?

   _____

3. In puff pastry the ratio of fat to flour is 2 : 3. How much flour would be needed if 500 g of fat were used?

   _____

4. A fruit punch is made from orange juice, cranberry juice and mango juice in the ratio 5 : 4 : 1. How much cranberry juice will there be in a 250 ml glass of fruit punch?

   _____

4 Scale diagrams

▷ The scale on a drawing or map is a ratio.

On a map with a scale of 1:100, every length of 1 unit on the map represents a length of 100 units on the ground.

Example 1: The scale on a road map is 2 cm to 5 km.
Two towns are 45 km apart.
What is their distance apart on the map?

Every 5 km on the ground is represented by 2 cm on the map. Find how many 'lots of' 5 km there are in 45 km and then multiply this by 2 cm.

$\frac{45}{5} \times 2 = 9 \times 2 = 18$

Answer: 18 cm

Example 2: A scale model car has a bonnet of length 10 cm. The scale is 1:20. What is the length of the bonnet on the original car?

Every length on the real car is 20 times the equivalent length on the model.

Length of bonnet on real car = 20 × 10 cm = 200 cm

Answer: 200 cm

Example 3: A student draws a scale diagram of the drama studio, using a scale of 1:50. The width of the drama studio is 40 m. What is the width on the diagram?

Every length in the drama studio is 50 times the length in the diagram.

The ratio is 1:50.

50 parts represent 40 m = 40 × 100 cm = 4 000 cm

1 part represents $\frac{4\,000}{50} = 80$ cm

Answer: 80 cm

> **Test tip**
>
> Check the units given in the answer.
> Here, map distances are in cm and real distances in km.

> **Tip**
>
> Changing to cm makes the calculation easier.

Now try it!

1. The scale on a map is 1:190 000. On the map, the distance between two towns is 20 cm.
   What is the actual distance between the two towns?

   _____

   _____

2. A scale diagram of a nursery shows the width of the nursery as 6.5 cm. The scale is 1:200.
   What is the actual width of the nursery, in metres?

   _____

   _____

3. A map of a town is drawn, using a scale of 1 cm to 0.5 miles. On the map, the distance between the library and the museum is 8 cm.
   What is the actual distance between the library and the museum?

   _____

   _____

4. A designer draws a scale diagram of a kitchen, using a scale of 1:50. The actual length of a wall unit is 3.5 m.
   What is the length of the wall unit on the scale diagram?

   _____

   _____

5. The heights of three girls on a photograph are 10 cm, 9 cm and 7 cm. The scale of the photograph is 1:16.
   What are the girls' real heights?

   _____

   _____

6. The map shows the start and finish points for a sponsored walk. The scale is 1 cm to 0.5 miles.

   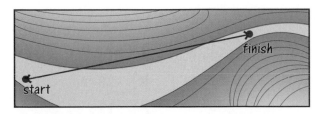

   What is the distance, in miles, between the start and finish points?

   _____

   _____

Remember what you have learned

First complete this ...

▷ A _____ is a way of comparing two or more quantities.

▷ You usually write ratios in their _____ form.

▷ You can use a ratio to scale quantities up or down. You _____ or _____ each amount by the same number.

▷ To compare units of measure, make sure they are in the same _____.

▷ Think of a ratio as being made up of a number of _____: 3 : 2 is a total of _____ parts.

▷ The scale on a drawing or map is a _____.

Now try it!

1. On a map, the distance between two towns is 27 centimetres. The scale of the map is 2 centimetres to 5 kilometres.

   What is the actual distance between the two towns?

   A ☐ 2.7 km
   B ☐ 10.8 km
   C ☐ 67.5 km
   D ☐ 135 km

2. A hotel had 15 432 guests in one year. Of these guests, 5 842 used the hotel swimming pool.

   What is the approximate ratio of those who used the pool to those who did not use the pool?

   A ☐ 3 : 5
   B ☐ 2 : 5
   C ☐ 5 : 3
   D ☐ 5 : 2

3. A designer draws a plan of a coffee shop, using a scale of 1 : 50. The actual length of the counter in the coffee shop is 4 metres.

   What is the length of the counter on the scale drawing?

   A ☐ 2 cm
   B ☐ 8 cm
   C ☐ 12.5 cm
   D ☐ 20 cm

4. A barman makes a fruit cocktail by mixing apple juice, pineapple juice and orange juice in the ratio 1 : 2 : 2. He uses 5 litres of orange juice.

   How much fruit cocktail does he make?

   A ☐ 10 litres
   B ☐ 12.5 litres
   C ☐ 25 litres
   D ☐ 37.5 litres

5. A nursery nurse makes 14 litres of orange drink for the children in a playgroup. She mixes orange concentrate and water in the ratio 2 : 5.

   How many litres of orange concentrate does she use?

   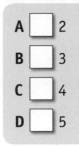

   A ☐ 2

   B ☐ 3

   C ☐ 4

   D ☐ 5

6. On a map with a scale of 1 : 500 000, the distance between a family's home and the airport is 30 cm.

   What is the actual distance between their home and the airport?

   A ☐ 15 km

   B ☐ 750 km

   C ☐ 150 km

   D ☐ 75 km

7. A car has an average fuel consumption of 5.6 litres per 100 km.

   Which of these calculations would you use to estimate how much fuel you would need for a journey of 88 km?

   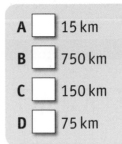

   A ☐ 5.6 ÷ 88 × 100

   B ☐ 5.6 ÷ 100 × 88

   C ☐ 88 ÷ 5.6 × 100

   D ☐ 88 × 100 ÷ 5.6

8. A recipe for 20 almond biscuits requires:
   • 150 g margarine
   • 150 g sugar
   • 1 egg
   • 300 g self-raising flour
   • 50 g ground almonds

   How much flour will be needed to make 65 biscuits?

   A ☐ 900 g

   B ☐ 975 g

   C ☐ 1 000 g

   D ☐ 1 050 g

9. A model of a boat is made to a scale of 1 : 40. The length of the real boat is 25 metres.

   What is the length of the model boat?

   A ☐ 6.25 cm

   B ☐ 10 cm

   C ☐ 62.5 cm

   D ☐ 100 cm

10. A man shares 480 g of dog food between a small dog and a larger dog in the ratio 3 : 5.

    How much does the larger dog get?

    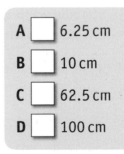

    A ☐ 180 g

    B ☐ 300 g

    C ☐ 288 g

    D ☐ 280 g

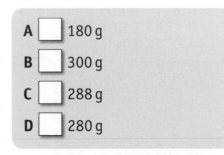

G Working with formulae

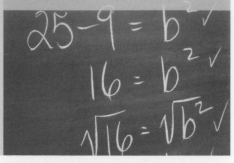

By the end of this section you will know how to:

▷▷ use formulae expressed in words

▷▷ apply the BIDMAS rule to evaluate an expression

▷▷ use formulae expressed in symbols.

1 Formulae in words

First read this ...

A formula is a way of describing a rule or relationship.

▷ A formula can be expressed either in words with the word 'equals', or in symbols with an equals sign (=).

Formulae is the plural of formula.

Example 1: The cost of hiring a car is £30 per day plus a £50 deposit. Work out the cost of hiring a car for 10 days.

Total cost = (number of days × £30) + £50

Total cost = (10 × £30) + £50

$\qquad$ = £300 + £50

$\qquad$ = £350

Answer: £350

Example 2: A telephone company sets a quarterly rental charge of £18.72, and each unit used costs 3.6p. Find the total charge for a quarter where 900 units are used.

The total cost of the units used is:

900 × 3.6 = 3 240 pence

$\qquad = £\frac{3\,240}{100}$

Cost of units used = £32.40

Total bill = rental charge + cost of units
$\qquad$ = £18.72 + £32.40
$\qquad$ = £51.12

Answer: £51.12

Tip

Dividing by 100 moves all the digits two places to the right.

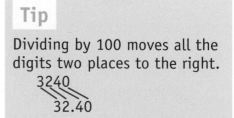

▶▶ *Now try it!*

1. The cost of hiring a carpet cleaner is £15 basic charge plus £18 per day. How much does it cost to hire the carpet cleaner for four days?

   _____

   _____

2. The cost of hiring a car is £20 per day plus 25p for every mile driven. A woman hires a car for six days and drives 100 miles. How much will she be charged?

   _____

   _____

Test tip

Look at the units used in the answer. Change all the quantities to this unit before calculating.

3. The time to cook a chicken is 20 minutes per $\frac{1}{2}$ kg plus 20 minutes. How long will it take to cook a chicken weighing $3\frac{1}{2}$ kg?

   _____

   _____

4. A man pays for his holiday by paying a deposit of £75 and then eight monthly payments of £35. What is the total cost of his holiday?

   _____

   _____

5. A mobile phone company charges £12 per month for its mobile phones, plus 6 pence per minute for phone calls made. What is the charge in a month where a woman makes 500 minutes of phone calls?

   _____

   _____

6. An electricity company has a standing charge of £8.50 per quarter plus 6.4 pence for every unit of electricity used. How much does the electricity company charge in a quarter where 600 units of electricity are used?

   _____

   _____

2 Formulae in symbols

⏸ *First read this ...*

Use the **BIDMAS rule** to help you remember which order to follow, to evaluate an expression.

▷ The BIDMAS rule is:

- ▷ **B**rackets
- ▷ **I**ndices
- ▷ **D**ivision or **M**ultiplication
- ▷ **A**ddition or **S**ubtraction.

Remember

Indices are powers:
$3^2 = 3 \times 3$
It is a common mistake to say
$3^2 = 3 \times 2$

Example 1: Evaluate these.
a $12 - 5 \times 4 + 2$ **b** $(12 - 5) \times 4 + 2$ **c** $(12 - 5) \times (4 + 2)$

a Multiplication before addition and subtraction.

$12 - 5 \times 4 + 2 = 12 - 20 + 2 = -6$

Answer: −6

Tip

Always follow this order or you will get the wrong answer.

b Brackets must be worked out first.

$(12 - 5) \times 4 + 2 = 7 \times 4 + 2 = 28 + 2 = 30$

Answer: 30

c The two sets of brackets must be worked out first.

$(12 - 5) \times (4 + 2) = 7 \times 6 = 42$

Answer: 42

Example 2: Work out the value of $2 \times 3^2 \times 4$.

The indices must be worked out first.
$2 \times 3^2 \times 4 = 2 \times 9 \times 4 = 72$

Answer: 72

Example 3: Use the formula $C = 30n + 50$ to work out the value of C when $n = 10$.

To find C, put the value of n in the formula.

$C = 30 \times 10 + 50$
$C = 300 + 50 = £350$

Answer: £350

Remember

$30n$ means $30 \times n$.

Example 4: The formula to convert a temperature in Celsius, C, to a temperature in Fahrenheit, F, is $F = \frac{9}{5}C + 32$. Use the formula to convert 45°C to the Fahrenheit equivalent.

Substituting $C = 45$:

$F = \frac{9}{5} \times 45 + 32$

$F = 81 + 32 = 113°F$

$$\frac{9}{\cancel{5}_1} \times \frac{\cancel{45}^9}{1} = \frac{9}{1} \times \frac{9}{1} = 81$$

Tip

You can multiply or divide in any order. Here, dividing first cancels out factors and makes the calculation easier.

Answer: 113°F

Example 5: The formula to convert a temperature in Fahrenheit, F, to the equivalent temperature in Celsius, C, is $C = \frac{5}{9}(F - 32)$. Use the formula to convert 59°F to the Celsius equivalent.

$C = \frac{5}{9}(F - 32)$

Substituting $F = 59$:

$C = \frac{5}{9}(59 - 32) = \frac{5}{9} \times 27 = \frac{5}{\cancel{9}_1} \times \frac{\cancel{27}^3}{1} = \frac{5}{1} \times \frac{3}{1} = 15$

Answer: 15° C

▶▶ Now try it!

1. Evaluate $\frac{(10 - 2)}{4}$

2. Evaluate $3 \times 2^2 \times 5$

3. Evaluate $3(5 + 4)$

4. Evaluate $\frac{1}{2}(4^2 - 6)$

5. The formula for calculating the area of a rectangle is $A = LW$, where L is the length of the rectangle and W is the width. Calculate the area of a rectangle with length 12 cm and width 4.5 cm.

6. A formula for converting centimetres, c, to inches, I, is $c = 2.5I$. Use the formula to convert 12.8 cm to inches.

7. The formula to calculate simple interest, I, when an amount of money, P, is invested at a rate, R, for a period of time, T, is

$I = \frac{PRT}{100}.$

Calculate the simple interest when £500 is invested for 3 years at a rate of 5%.

8. The formula that converts a temperature in Celsius, C, to the equivalent temperature in Fahrenheit, F, is $F = \frac{9}{5}C + 32$. Use the formula to convert 55°C to Fahrenheit.

Tip

Work out the brackets first.

Tip

Remember to apply **BIDMAS**.

Remember

$3(5 + 4)$ means $3 \times (5 + 4)$

Test tip

Always check that your answer makes sense, by substituting back into the formula.

First complete this ...

▷ A formula can be expressed either in words with the word
  '_____', or in symbols with an _____
  sign (____).

▷ The BIDMAS rule is:

  ▷ _____

  ▷ _____

  ▷ Division or Multiplication

  ▷ Addition or Subtraction.

▷ Indices are powers, for example, $3^2 = 3 \times$ ____.

▷ $30n$ means ____ $\times n$.

Now try it!

1. To calculate the cost of printing leaflets, a printer uses
   the formula $C = 25 + 0.08n$, where C is the cost, in
   pounds, and n is the number of leaflets.

   How much would he charge for printing 500 leaflets?

   A ☐ £29

   B ☐ £65

   C ☐ £87.50

   D ☐ £425

2. A recipe book says that the cooking time for a joint of
   beef is given by:

   time, in minutes $= \dfrac{105 \times \text{weight in kilograms}}{2} + 25$

   How long would it take to cook a 4 kilogram joint of beef?

   A ☐ 2 hours 35 mins

   B ☐ 2 hours 55 mins

   C ☐ 3 hours 35 mins

   D ☐ 3 hours 55 mins

3. A water bottle is shaped like
   a cylinder.

   Volume of cylinder $= \pi r^2 h$

   where r is the base radius and
   h is the height.

   Taking the value of π as 3,
   work out approximately how
   much water the water bottle
   will hold.

20 cm

4 cm

   A ☐ 240 cm³

   B ☐ 720 cm³

   C ☐ 960 cm³

   D ☐ 2 880 cm³

4. The formula that converts a temperature in Fahrenheit, *F*, to the equivalent temperature in Celsius, *C*, is

$$C = \frac{5(F - 32)}{9}$$

The temperature in London one morning was 77 degrees Fahrenheit.

What was the temperature in degrees Celsius?

A ☐ 11°C

B ☐ 25°C

C ☐ 59°C

D ☐ 81°C

5. A shopkeeper buys bracelets for £2.50 each and sells them for £4.50.

$$\text{Percentage profit} = \frac{\text{selling price} - \text{buying price}}{\text{buying price}} \times 100\%$$

What is the shopkeeper's percentage profit?

A ☐ 44%

B ☐ 56%

C ☐ 70%

D ☐ 80%

6. A woman earns a basic rate of £16 per hour for a 40-hour week. For each hour worked over 40 hours she earns 1½ times the basic rate.

How much does the woman earn in a week when she works 45 hours?

A ☐ £640

B ☐ £720

C ☐ £760

D ☐ £960

7. A company sells personalised mugs with names printed on them. The company charges £12 for each mug plus 9p for each letter printed on it.

How much will it cost to have the name 'Brooklyn' printed on a mug?

A ☐ £12.72

B ☐ £12.81

C ☐ £19.20

D ☐ £84

8. A cleaning company charges a fixed fee of £50 plus £7.50 per hour for cleaning.

How much does the company charge for 5 hours of cleaning?

A ☐ £62.50

B ☐ £85

C ☐ £87.50

D ☐ £207.50

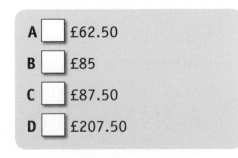

H Working with units and scales

You should already know how to:

✓ read, measure and record time in common date formats and in the 12-hour and 24-hour clock

✓ choose and use appropriate units and instruments to measure length, weight, capacity, time and temperature

✓ add, subtract and convert common units of measure.

By the end of this section you will know how to:

▶▶ calculate, measure and record time in different formats

▶▶ estimate, measure and compare length, weight, capacity and temperature, using metric and imperial units

▶▶ read scales and use conversion factors.

1 Time

▌▌ *First read this ...*

You need to know the units for time and the connections between them.

▷ 60 seconds = 1 minute ▷ 7 days = 1 week

▷ 60 minutes = 1 hour ▷ 52 weeks = 1 year

▷ 365 days = 1 year ▷ 12 months = 1 year
   (366 in a leap year)

Example 1: A train leaves Manchester at 09.45 and arrives in London at 12.06. How long does the train take to get from Manchester to London?

09.45 to 11.45 is 2 hours.

11.45 to 12.00 is 15 minutes.

12.00 to 12.06 is 6 minutes.

Total time = 2 hours + 15 minutes + 6 minutes
           = 2 hours 21 minutes

Answer: 2 hours 21 minutes

Tip

A timeline can help:

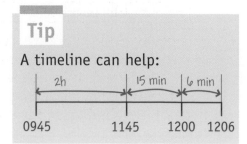

Example 2: A boy is 9 years 2 months old. His sister is 2 years 5 months younger. How old is his sister?

You need to subtract 2 years 5 months from 9 years 2 months.

First subtract 2 years to give 7 years 2 months.

Then subtract 2 months to give 7 years.   (5 = 2 + 3)

Finally, subtract the remaining 3 months to give 6 years 9 months.

Answer: 6 years 9 months

▶▶ *Now try it!*

1. A family plan to take a train to Newcastle which leaves at 07.27. They need to allow 40 minutes to get from home to the station. What time should they leave home?

Test tip

In test questions involving time you will be looking at train and bus timetables, as well as finding the time taken to complete activities.

2. A telephone bill shows the longest telephone call was 33 minutes 7 seconds and the shortest was 6 minutes 50 seconds. What is the difference between the two times?

3. A builder drives for 20 minutes to the local DIY store. He takes $1\frac{3}{4}$ hours in the DIY store and then drives to work, which takes $1\frac{1}{2}$ hours. How long does his journey take, in total?

4. The youngest child in a nursery is 1 year 9 months old. The oldest child is 4 years 5 months old. What is the difference between these two ages?

Tip

In the 24-hour clock the day runs from midnight to midnight and is divided into 24 hours, numbered from 0 to 23.
17.25 = 5.25pm (17 – 12 = 5)

5. The timetable shows the times of coaches from Manchester Piccadilly to Liverpool John Lennon Airport in the afternoon.

Manchester Piccadilly Rail Station	1400	1500	1600	1700	1800	1900	2000	2100	2200	2300
Manchester Sackville Street	1410	1510	1610	1710	1810	1910	2010	2110	2210	2310
Salford Regent Road Sainsbury's	1418	1518	1618	1718	1818	1918	2018	2118	2218	2318
Eccles Interchange	1428	1528	1628	1728	1828	1928	2028	2128	2228	2328
Burtonwood Services	1453	1553	1653	1753	1853	1953	2053	2153	2253	2353
Liverpool John Lennon Airport	1515	1615	1715	1815	1915	2015	2115	2215	2315	0015

Source: Arriva Passenger Services

A family living in Manchester have booked a flight from Liverpool John Lennon Airport. The flight leaves at 7pm and they need to be at the airport at least two hours before the flight departure. What is the time of the latest coach the family can take to get to the airport on time?

2 Temperature

First read this ...

Temperature is usually recorded in **degrees Celsius**, although **degrees Fahrenheit** are still sometimes used.

▷ To read a temperature scale, first work out what the individual marks on the scale represent.

Example 1: The thermometer shows the maximum and minimum temperatures recorded in Moscow on a particular day.
What is the difference between the maximum and minimum temperatures?

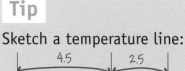

10 marks represent 5 degrees

so 1 mark represents $\frac{5}{10}$ = 0.5 degrees

Reading from the scale, the maximum temperature is 2.5°C and the minimum temperature is −4.5°C.

The signs are different so you *add* the two numbers together to find the difference in temperature.

2.5 + 4.5 = 7

Answer: 7°C

Tip

Sketch a temperature line:

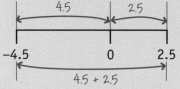

Now try it!

1. What is the temperature marked on this thermometer?

_____

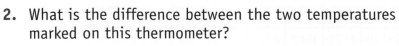

2. What is the difference between the two temperatures marked on this thermometer?

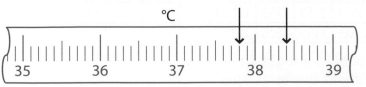

_____

3 Length

▷ Length is a measure of distance.

You need to know the metric units for length and the connections between them.

▷ 10 mm = 1 cm

▷ 100 cm = 1 m

▷ 1000 m = 1 km

Questions often involve reading scales.

Test tip

Questions about length may be set in **metric** or **imperial** units.

Example 1: Work out the distance between the two markers shown on the ruler.

[ruler showing 0cm to 9 with markers at 2 and 7]

10 marks represent 1 centimetre.

1 mark represents $\frac{1}{10}$ = 0.1 cm.

The first mark is at 2.4 cm, the second is at 6.7 cm, so the distance between them is 6.7 − 2.4 = 4.3 cm.

Answer: 4.3 cm

1. Work out the distance between the markings on this metre scale.

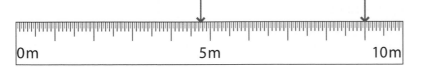

2. What is the distance between the two points marked on this scale?

[ruler showing 0cm 1 2 3 4 5 6 7 8 9 with two markers]

4 Weight

First read this ...

▷ Weight is a measure of the **mass** of an object.

You need to know the metric units for weight and the connections between them.

▷ 1 000 g = 1 kg

▷ 1 000 kg = 1 tonne

Example 1: What is the weight, in kilograms, marked on this scale?

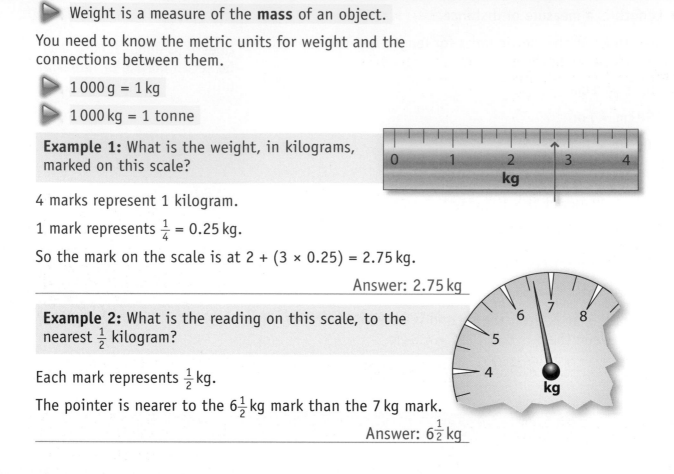

4 marks represent 1 kilogram.

1 mark represents $\frac{1}{4}$ = 0.25 kg.

So the mark on the scale is at 2 + (3 × 0.25) = 2.75 kg.

Answer: 2.75 kg

Example 2: What is the reading on this scale, to the nearest $\frac{1}{2}$ kilogram?

Each mark represents $\frac{1}{2}$ kg.

The pointer is nearer to the $6\frac{1}{2}$ kg mark than the 7 kg mark.

Answer: $6\frac{1}{2}$ kg

Now try it!

1. What is the reading on this scale, in grams?

    _____

2. What is the reading on this scale, which is marked in kilograms?

    _____

3. What is the difference between the two readings on this scale?

    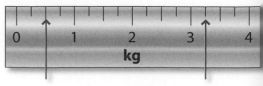

    _____

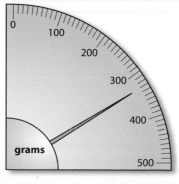

5 Capacity

First read this ...

▷ The capacity of a container is the amount of fluid it can hold.

You need to know the metric units for capacity and the connections between them.

▷ 100 cl = 1 litre

▷ 1 000 ml = 1 litre

▷ 1 000 cm³ = 1 litre

Remember

Capacity is a measure of volume.

Example 1: What is the reading on this scale, in millilitres?

5 marks represent 50 millilitres.

1 mark represents $\frac{50}{5}$ = 10 ml.

The reading is 170 ml.

Answer: 170 ml

Now try it!

1. What is the difference between the two marks on the scale, in millilitres?

_____

_____

2. A car's fuel tank holds 40 litres. The fuel gauges show the petrol in the tank at the start and the end of a journey. How much petrol did the car use during the journey?

_____

3. A lorry's fuel tank holds 100 litres of diesel. The diagram shows the amount of fuel in the tank at the start of a journey. Approximately how much petrol is in the tank?

_____

First read this ...

You convert between metric and imperial measures using a **conversion factor**.

▷ A conversion factor is a number by which you multiply or divide measures to change them to another unit.

Example 1: Convert 2.55 hours to hours and minutes.

2.55 hours = 2 hours + 0.55 hours

The conversion factor to change a fraction or decimal fraction of an hour to minutes is 60.

$0.55 \times 60 = (0.5 \times 60) + (0.05 \times 60) = 30 + 3 = 33$ minutes

Answer: 2 hours 33 minutes

Example 2: A car travels at a speed of 60 mph. Approximately what is 60 mph in km per hour? 1 mile is approximately 1.6 kilometres.

Multiply 60 by 1.6.

$60 \times 1.6 = (60 \times 1) + (60 \times 0.6) = 60 + 36 = 96$ km per hour

Answer: 96 km per hour

Example 3: A tennis player weighs 60 kg. She is playing in a tournament in the USA where imperial units are used. What is her weight, in stones and pounds? 1 kilogram is approximately 2.2 pounds and 14 pounds = 1 stone.

First, change kilograms to pounds by multiplying by 2.2.

$60 \times 2.2 = (60 \times 2) + (60 \times 0.2) = 120 + 12 = 132$ pounds

14 pounds = 1 stone   so   140 pounds = 10 stones

132 pounds = 10 stones – 8 pounds = 9 stones 6 pounds

Answer: 9 stones 6 pounds

Example 4: When on holiday in Germany, a family pays €1.34 per litre for petrol. What calculation would you do to find the cost of the petrol in pounds per gallon? 1 euro = 69 pence and 4.5 litres is roughly 1 gallon.

First, find the cost in pounds per litre.

Next, find the cost in pounds per gallon.

€1.34 per litre = 1.34 × 0.69 pounds per litre.

4.5 litres is roughly 1 gallon so the calculation must be:

$$\frac{1.34 \times 0.69}{4.5}$$

Answer: $\dfrac{1.34 \times 0.69}{4.5}$ pounds per gallon

▶▶ *Now try it!*

1. A car travels at an average speed of 50 mph. Approximately how long, in hours and minutes, does it take to travel a distance of 115 miles?

   _____

2. A television is described as having a 22-inch screen. What is 22 inches in centimetres? Use 1 inch = 2.5 cm.

   _____

3. A football pitch has a length of 22 yards. What is the length of the football pitch in metres? Use 1 yard = 3 feet, 1 foot = 12 inches and 1 inch = 2.5 cm.

   _____

4. An electrician needs 90 feet of cable. Approximately how many metres of cable does he need?
   Use 1 metre = 40 inches.

   _____

5. Tomatoes are priced at £1.43 per kilogram. What is the price of the tomatoes per pound weight?
   Use 1 kg = 2.2 pounds.

   _____

6. A recipe for chocolate cake needs 8 ounces of self-raising flour. How many grams of flour are needed for the chocolate cake? Use 1 ounce = 25 g.

   _____

7. A ballerina weighs 7 stone 1 pound. What does she weigh in kilograms? Use 1 kg = 2.2 pounds, 14 pounds = 1 stone.

   _____

   _____

8. A recipe for chocolate mousse needs $7\frac{1}{2}$ fluid ounces of double cream. Approximately what is $7\frac{1}{2}$ fluid ounces in millilitres? Use 1 fluid ounce = 28 millilitres.

   _____

   _____

9. The instructions for mixing baby milk formula say that 5 scoops of powdered milk should be mixed with half a pint of water. How many millilitres are needed for each scoop of powdered milk? Use 1 pint = 570 millilitres.

   _____

   _____

First complete this ...

▷ You need to know these units:

- ▷ 60 seconds = 1 _____
- ▷ 60 _____ = 1 hour
- ▷ 7 _____ = 1 week
- ▷ 52 weeks = 1 _____
- ▷ 365 days = 1 _____
  (366 in a _____ year)
- ▷ 12 _____ = 1 year
- ▷ _____ mm = 1 cm

- ▷ _____ cm = 1 m
- ▷ _____ m = 1 km
- ▷ _____ g = 1 kg
- ▷ _____ kg = 1 tonne
- ▷ _____ cl = 1 litre
- ▷ _____ ml = 1 litre
- ▷ _____ cm³ = 1 litre

▷ To read a temperature _____, first work out what the individual marks on the _____ represent.

▷ Length is a measure of _____.

▷ Weight is a measure of the _____ of an object.

▷ The _____ of a container is the amount of fluid it can hold.

▷ A _____ factor is a number by which you multiply or divide to change between units.

Now try it!

1. The preparation time for French roast lamb is $\frac{3}{4}$ hour and the cooking time is 3 hours 25 minutes.

   What is the latest time a chef could begin to prepare French roast lamb, if it needs to be ready for customers at 8.30 pm?

   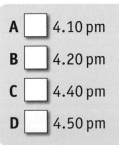

   A ☐ 4.10 pm

   B ☐ 4.20 pm

   C ☐ 4.40 pm

   D ☐ 4.50 pm

2. A truck driver is driving a British vehicle in France. His fuel tank holds 18 gallons and is $\frac{1}{4}$ full.

   How many litres does he need to buy to fill up with fuel? 1 gallon is roughly 4.5 litres.

   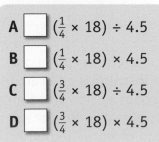

   A ☐ $(\frac{1}{4} \times 18) \div 4.5$

   B ☐ $(\frac{1}{4} \times 18) \times 4.5$

   C ☐ $(\frac{3}{4} \times 18) \div 4.5$

   D ☐ $(\frac{3}{4} \times 18) \times 4.5$

3. The Health Service needs to collect 10 000 units of blood per day to meet demand. 1 unit of blood is 450 ml.

How many litres of blood does the Health Service need per week? 1 litre = 1 000 ml

A ☐ 3 150

B ☐ 31 500

C ☐ 3 150 000

D ☐ 315 000

4. The tallest player in the England football team in 2006 was 6 foot 7 inches.

What calculation gives his height, in metres? 1 inch is roughly 2.54 centimetres and 1 foot = 12 inches.

A ☐ $\dfrac{66 \times 2.54}{100}$

B ☐ $\dfrac{6 \times 12 \times 2.54}{100}$

C ☐ $\dfrac{67 \times 12 \times 2.54}{100}$

D ☐ $\dfrac{(6 \times 12 + 7) \times 2.54}{100}$

5. The average flying height of a plane is 39 000 feet.

What is the average flying height of the plane, in metres? 13 feet is approximately 4 metres.

A ☐ 3 000 m

B ☐ 12 000 m

C ☐ 39 000 m

D ☐ 126 750 m

6. This thermometer shows the temperature inside a deep freeze before and after it has been defrosted.

−20   0°C   20

What is the difference between the temperatures?

A ☐ 8°C

B ☐ 11°C

C ☐ 20°C

D ☐ 24°C

7. The diagram shows the voltage across a circuit on a voltmeter.

What is the voltage, to the nearest 10 volts?

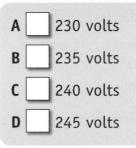

300

200   VOLTS

A ☐ 230 volts

B ☐ 235 volts

C ☐ 240 volts

D ☐ 245 volts

8. A recipe for one omelette needs 5 fluid ounces of milk.

What calculation would you do to work out how many omelettes you can make from 1 litre of milk? 1 fluid ounce is approximately 28 ml.

A ☐ $\dfrac{5 \times 28}{100}$

B ☐ $\dfrac{5 + 28}{100}$

C ☐ $\dfrac{1\,000}{5 \times 28}$

D ☐ $\dfrac{1\,000}{5 + 28}$

I Working with perimeter, area and volume

You should already know how to:

- ✔ work out the perimeters of simple shapes
- ✔ work out the areas of rectangles
- ✔ work out volumes of simple solids, such as cuboids
- ✔ solve problems, using the mathematical properties of regular 2-D shapes
- ✔ draw 2-D shapes in different orientations.

By the end of this section you will know how to:

- ▷▷ find perimeters and areas of regular shapes
- ▷▷ find areas of composite shapes
- ▷▷ find volumes of regular shapes
- ▷▷ solve problems in three dimensions.

1 Perimeter

First read this ...

▷ The **perimeter** of a shape is the total length of its **boundary**.

For a rectangle, the perimeter, P, is given by the formula:
$P = 2(l + w)$

where l is the length and w is the width.

▷ The perimeter of a circle is called its **circumference**.

The circumference, C, of a circle can be written in two ways:

- ■ $C = \pi d$ where d = **diameter**
- ■ $C = 2\pi r$ where r = **radius**

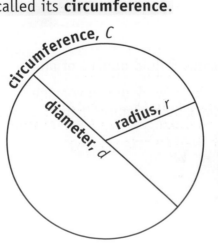

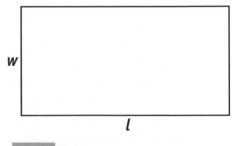

> **Tip**
>
> π is a special number, equal to the ratio of the circumference of a circle to its diameter.
> π is an **irrational number**, which means it cannot be written as a fraction.
> π is approximately equal to 3.142.

Example 1: A circular pond, 3.6 metres in diameter, has a fence around it, at a constant distance of 0.6 metres from the edge. Find the length of the fence. Circumference = $2\pi r$ and $\pi = 3$

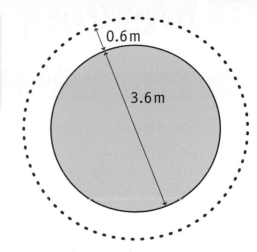

The diameter of the pond is 3.6 m.

Radius = $\frac{3.6}{2}$ = 1.8 m.

The radius of the circle formed by the fence = 1.8 + 0.6 = 2.4 m.

Length of fence = $2\pi r$ = 2 × 3 × 2.4
= 6 × 2.4 = 14.4 m

Answer: 14.4 m

▶▶ *Now try it!*

1. A cake shop sells birthday cakes that are 20 cm in diameter. What is the shortest length of ribbon that would fit round the outside of the cake? $C = 2\pi r$ and $\pi = 3$

2. The plan shows the dimensions of an L-shaped sitting room. The house owner wants to buy skirting board to go around the edge of the room, leaving gaps at the doors. What is the shortest length of skirting board he can buy?

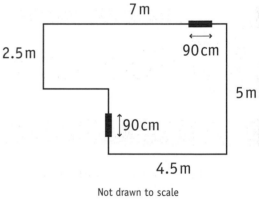

Not drawn to scale

3. A semicircular window has a diameter of 1.6 m. The window frame is made of plastic strips along the outside edge. What is the total length of the plastic strip around the window frame? Use $\pi = 3$

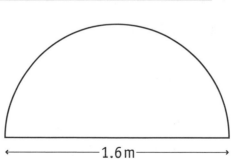

4. A lawn has the shape of a rectangle with one semicircular end. There is concrete edging around the outside of the lawn. What is the length of the concrete edging? Use $\pi = 3$

8 m

16 m

2 Area

First read this ...

▷ The **area** of a shape is a measure of the amount of space it covers.

▷ For a circle the area, *A*, is given by the formula: $A = \pi r^2$, where *r* is the **radius**.

Example 1: The top of a birthday cake, which is 30 cm in diameter, is to be covered in fondant icing. What area of icing will be needed? Area = πr^2, $\pi = 3$

The diameter = $\frac{30}{2}$ = 15.

Area = πr^2 = 3 × 15^2 = 3 × 225 = 675 cm^2

Answer: 675 cm^2

You work out the area of a **composite shape** by splitting it into simple shapes.

Example 2: This kitchen floor is to be covered in cushioned vinyl. What area of cushioned vinyl is needed?

Split the L-shaped room into two rectangles A and B.

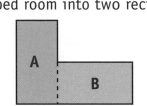

Area of A	Area of B
= 4.5 × 5	= 2.5 × (7 − 4.5)
= 22.5 m^2	= 2.5 × 2.5 = 6.25 m^2

Total area = 22.5 + 6.25 = 28.75 m^2

Answer: 28.75 m^2

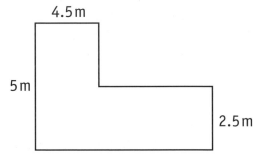

4.5 m
5 m
2.5 m
7 m
Not drawn to scale

Example 3: The diagram shows the plan of a patio. The patio is to be paved with square paving slabs with sides of 0.5 metres. How many paving slabs will it take?

Work out how many paving slabs would be needed for the full rectangle and then take away the number that would be needed in the cut-out piece.

The slabs are 0.5 m long, so two are needed for every metre.

For the 10 m width, 20 slabs are needed.

For the 6 m length, 12 slabs are needed.

Number of slabs for the whole rectangle = 20 × 12 = 240.

The cut-out piece is 2 m by 2 m.

This would take 4 × 4 = 16 slabs.

The total is 240 − 16 = 224 paving slabs.

Answer: 224

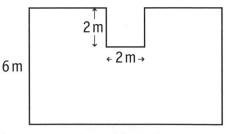

2 m
6 m
← 2 m →
10 m
Not drawn to scale

Tip

Metric units of area are mm^2, cm^2, m^2 and km^2.

Remember

Follow the BIDMAS rule and work out r^2 first. r^2 means $r × r$.

Test tip

Test questions are often based on gardening or decorating problems and may involve conversions between units.

You will need to find the area of triangles.

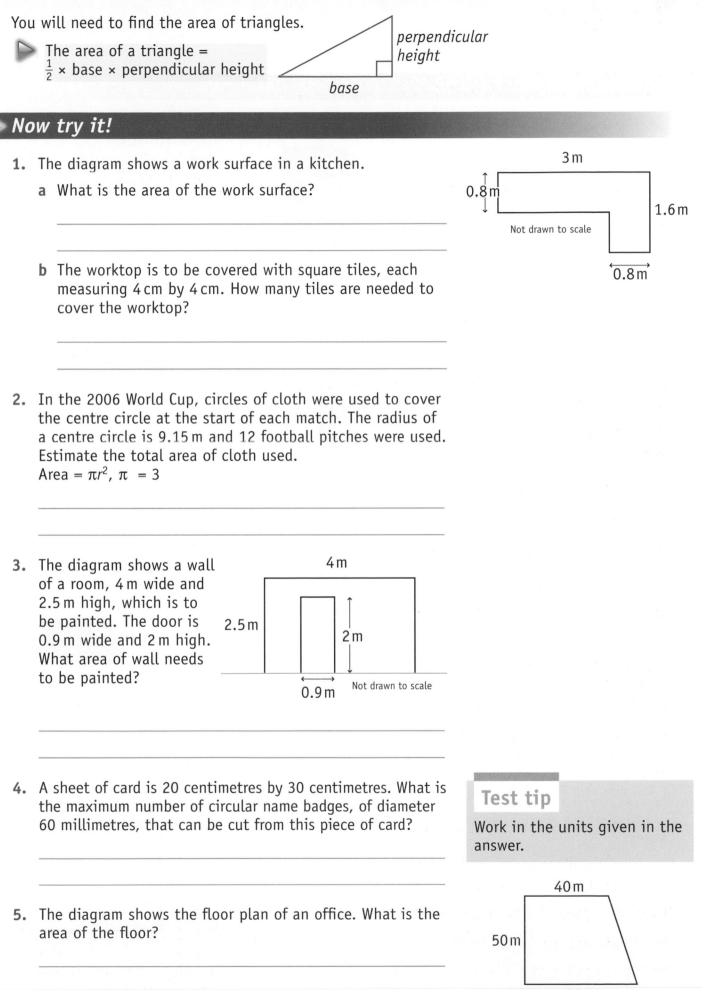

▷ The area of a triangle = $\frac{1}{2}$ × base × perpendicular height

perpendicular
height

base

▶▶ Now try it!

1. The diagram shows a work surface in a kitchen.

   a What is the area of the work surface?

   _____

   _____

   3 m

   0.8 m

   1.6 m

   Not drawn to scale

   0.8 m

   b The worktop is to be covered with square tiles, each measuring 4 cm by 4 cm. How many tiles are needed to cover the worktop?

   _____

   _____

2. In the 2006 World Cup, circles of cloth were used to cover the centre circle at the start of each match. The radius of a centre circle is 9.15 m and 12 football pitches were used. Estimate the total area of cloth used.
   Area = πr^2, π = 3

   _____

   _____

3. The diagram shows a wall of a room, 4 m wide and 2.5 m high, which is to be painted. The door is 0.9 m wide and 2 m high. What area of wall needs to be painted?

   4 m

   2.5 m

   2 m

   0.9 m   Not drawn to scale

   _____

   _____

4. A sheet of card is 20 centimetres by 30 centimetres. What is the maximum number of circular name badges, of diameter 60 millimetres, that can be cut from this piece of card?

   _____

   _____

   Test tip

   Work in the units given in the answer.

5. The diagram shows the floor plan of an office. What is the area of the floor?

   _____

   _____

   40 m

   50 m

   Not drawn to scale   55 m

73

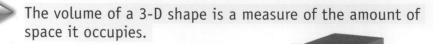

First read this …

▷ The volume of a 3-D shape is a measure of the amount of space it occupies.

▷ The volume of a cuboid is $l \times w \times h$ where l = length, w = width and h = height.

h

l *w*

> **Remember**
>
> Metric units of volume are mm^3, cm^3, m^3 and km^3.

▷ The volume, V, of a cylinder is:
$V = \pi r^2 h$
where r is the base **radius** and h is the **height**.

r

h

> **Remember**
>
> $\pi r^2 h$ means $\pi \times r^2 \times h$
> Follow the BIDMAS rule and work out r^2 first.

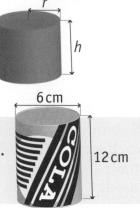

6 cm

12 cm

Not drawn to scale

> **Example 1:** A can of cola has a diameter of 6 cm and a height of 12 cm. What is the volume of the can?
> Volume = $\pi r^2 h$, $\pi = 3$

The diameter is 6 cm so the radius is 3 cm.

Volume = $\pi r^2 h = 3 \times 3^2 \times 12 = 3 \times 9 \times 12 = 324 \, cm^3$

Answer: $324 \, cm^3$

> **Remember**
>
> 1 litre = $1\,000 \, cm^3$ = $1\,000$ ml
> This means the can will hold 324 ml of liquid.

You may need to solve problems in **three dimensions**.

> **Example 2:** A tin of shoe polish is 8 cm in diameter and 2 cm high. The shoe polish must be stored in an upright position. How many tins of shoe polish will fit into a carton that is 40 cm long by 32 cm wide by 10 cm high?

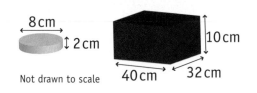

8 cm

↕ 2 cm

10 cm

Not drawn to scale   40 cm   32 cm

The base of the carton is 40 cm by 32 cm.
The tins are 8 cm wide.
This means that $\frac{40}{8}$ = 5 tins will fit along one edge and $\frac{32}{8}$ = 4 tins will fit along the other edge.

So a total of 5 × 4 = 20 tins will fit on the bottom of the carton.

The carton is 10 cm high, which means $\frac{10}{2}$ = 5 tins will fit, one on top of another.

The total number of tins in the carton is 20 × 5 = 100.

Answer: 100

> **Test tip**
>
> A sketch diagram can help you understand the question:
>
>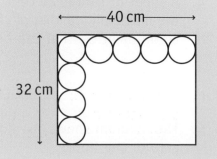
>
> 40 cm
>
> 32 cm

▶▶ Now try it!

1. An ice cream cone has a radius of 4 cm and a depth of 9 cm. The volume of a cone is $\frac{1}{3}\pi r^2 h$. What is the volume of the ice cream cone? Use $\pi = 3$.

_____

_____

4 cm

9 cm

Not drawn to scale

2. What is the volume of the recycling box shown in the diagram?

_____

_____

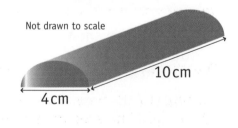

20 cm

40 cm   60 cm

Not drawn to scale

3. A waste bin is in the shape of a cylinder. The diameter of the base is 20 cm and the height is 25 cm. What is the volume of the waste bin?
Volume of cylinder = $\pi r^2 h$ and $\pi = 3$

_____

_____

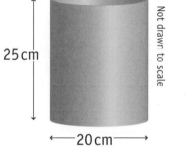

25 cm

20 cm

Not drawn to scale

4. A company makes rounded chocolate bars, as shown in the diagram. The ends are semicircular, with diameter 4 cm, and the bars are 10 cm long. What is the volume of chocolate in one bar? Volume of cylinder = $\pi r^2 h$ and $\pi = 3$

_____

_____

Not drawn to scale

10 cm

4 cm

5. A crate is 24 cm by 18 cm by 15 cm. It is to be packed with boxes that are 8 cm by 6 cm by 5 cm. What is the largest number of boxes that can fit in the crate?

_____

_____

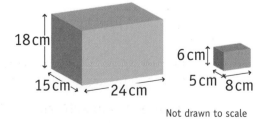

18 cm

15 cm   24 cm

6 cm

5 cm 8 cm

Not drawn to scale

6. A firm makes circular drink mats, of radius 4.5 cm, that are 3 mm thick. They want to produce a rectangular box to hold a pile of 12 mats. What are the minimum dimensions of the box?

_____

_____

First complete this ...

▷ The _____ of a shape is the total length of its boundary.

▷ The perimeter of a circle is called its _____.

▷ The _____ of a shape is the amount of space it covers.

▷ The _____ of a 3-D shape is the amount of space it occupies.

▷ You should know these formulae:

   ▷ _____ of a _____ = πd or $2\pi r$

   ▷ _____ of a _____ = length × width

   ▷ _____ of a _____ = $\frac{1}{2}$ × base × perpendicular height

   ▷ _____ of a _____ = πr^2

   ▷ _____ of a _____ = length × width × height

   ▷ _____ of a _____ = $\pi r^2 h$

Now try it!

1. The diagram shows the floor plan of an office.

   What is the area of the floor?

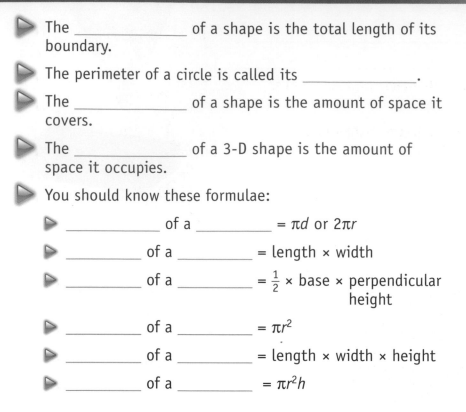

Not drawn to scale

A		16.5 m²
B		20 m²
C		20.5 m²
D		22 m²

2. The diagram shows a running track made up of a rectangle with two semicircular ends.

   What is the total length around the outside edge of the running track?
   Circumference of circle = $2\pi r$ and $\pi = 3$

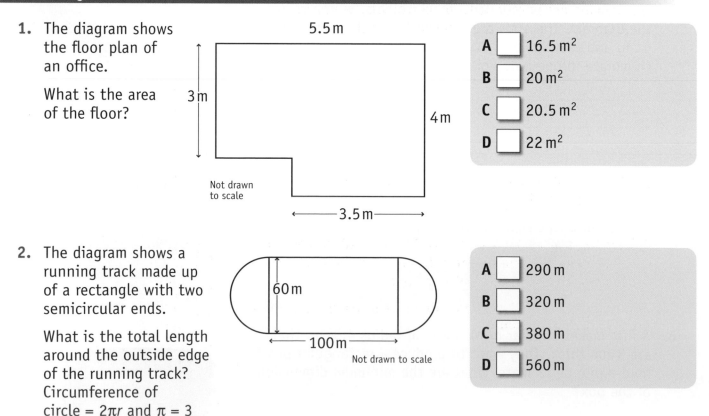

Not drawn to scale

A		290 m
B		320 m
C		380 m
D		560 m

3. What is the total area enclosed by the running track?
    Area of circle = πr^2 and $\pi = 3$

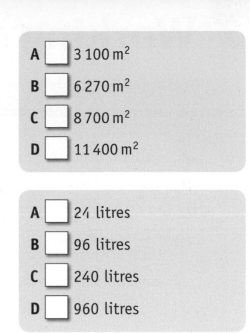

    A ☐ 3 100 m²

    B ☐ 6 270 m²

    C ☐ 8 700 m²

    D ☐ 11 400 m²

4. A cylindrical water butt has a diameter of 40 cm and is 200 cm high.

    What is the maximum amount of water it can hold?
    Volume of cylinder = $\pi r^2 h$ and $\pi = 3$. 1 litre = 1 000 cm³.

    A ☐ 24 litres

    B ☐ 96 litres

    C ☐ 240 litres

    D ☐ 960 litres

5. The diagram shows the dimensions of the baskets inside a freezer.

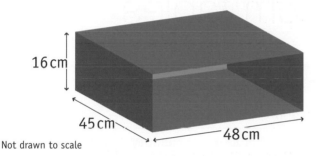

    16 cm

    45 cm

    48 cm

    Not drawn to scale

    The baskets are packed with blocks of ice-cream, in packets with dimensions as shown in the diagram.

    Not drawn to scale

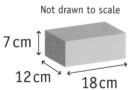

    7 cm

    12 cm   18 cm

    A ☐ 6

    B ☐ 8

    C ☐ 12

    D ☐ 16

    What is the maximum number of ice-cream blocks that can fit into the basket?

6. Baking trays measuring 25 cm by 20 cm by 12 cm deep are used to make rice pudding in a hospital kitchen. The trays are filled with milk to a depth of 10 cm.

    How many trays of rice pudding can be made from 25 litres of milk? 1 litre = 1 000 cm³

    A ☐ 3

    B ☐ 4

    C ☐ 5

    D ☐ 6

J Working with data

You should already know how to:

✓ extract and interpret information, for example, in tables, diagrams, charts and line graphs

✓ collect, organise and represent discrete data in tables, charts, diagrams and line graphs.

By the end of this section you will know how to:

⟫ extract discrete and continuous data from tables, charts, diagrams and line graphs

⟫ interpret information given by data in tables, charts, diagrams and line graphs.

1 Reading values from tables

First read this ...

You need to be able to extract information from tables.

Example 1: A woman wants to buy a new computer. She chooses from the models in this table.
She wants a computer with more than 1 000 Mb of memory, and more than 2.0 Gb capacity on the hard drive. She wants to pay less than £1 000. Which model should she buy?

Model number	Memory chip	Hard drive capacity	Price
DX23	512 Mb	1.6 Gb	£724
DX24	1 024 Mb	1.8 Gb	£856
DX25	1 024 Mb	2.4 Gb	£999
DX45	2 048 Mb	2.8 Gb	£1 120

Look at the amounts of memory for each model.
DX23 does not have enough.
Look at the hard drive capacity. DX24 is too small.
DX45 costs more than £1 000.
So only DX25 satisfies all the requirements.   Answer: DX25

Tip

Work through the requirements systematically.

Now try it!

1. Here is an extract from a holiday brochure giving prices per person for a holiday in Palma, Majorca.

   a Work out the cost for one person to stay for two weeks in Sunny Chalets, arriving on 1 July.

   b Work out the cost for two people to stay for one week in Bay View Hotel, arriving on 17 June.

Arrival date	Cost per person at Sunny Chalets		Cost per person at Bay View Hotel	
	7 days	additional 7 days	7 days	additional 7 days
1.6 to 16.6	£240	£80	£380	£140
17.6 to 30.6	£270	£80	£420	£150
1.7 to 16.7	£300	£100	£450	£150
17.7 to 31.7	£280	£100	£435	£135

2 Types of data

First read this ...

There are two general types of data.

- **Numerical data** such as marks in a test, waiting time in a doctor's surgery, and

- **Non-numerical data** such as colours of hair, makes of car.

Numerical data may be either **discrete** or **continuous**.

▷ **Discrete data** can only take particular values.

Shoe sizes, such as 5, $5\frac{1}{2}$, 6, $6\frac{1}{2}$ are discrete data. There are no values in between. The shoe size $5\frac{1}{4}$ does not exist!

▷ **Continuous data** can take any value.

Weight does not suddenly jump from 66 kg to 67 kg. It goes through all the values in between such as 66.723 145... kg.

Data can be grouped. This data shows the time taken to the nearest minute for 30 students to complete a practice test.

Time taken	Number of students
45–49	1
50–54	3
55–59	12
60–64	8
65–69	4
70–74	2

Tip

Each item of discrete data has an exact value.

Tip

Continuous data cannot be measured exactly. The accuracy depends on the measuring device.

Now try it!

1. Decide whether each of these types of data is discrete or continuous.

   a Height of a tree

   b Number of people in a room

   c Temperature of an oven

   d Time to wait for a bus

   e Number of goals scored in a football match

   f Your height

2. The grouped data frequency table shows the heights of year 11 students correct to the nearest centimetre.

   a How many year 11 students are there?

   b In which interval would a student with a height of 1.698 m lie?

Height in metres	Frequency
1.30–1.39	1
1.40–1.49	3
1.50–1.59	41
1.60–1.69	67
1.70–1.79	54
1.80–1.89	20
1.90–1.99	6

First read this ...

A **tally chart** is a useful way to collect data.

You can put the information into a **frequency table**.

Example 1: Here are the results of a survey on the number of pets per household.

Number of pets	Tally	Number of households
0	⫲⫲⫲ ⫲⫲⫲ ⫲⫲⫲ ⫲⫲⫲	20
1	⫲⫲⫲ ⫲⫲⫲ ⫲⫲⫲ ⫲⫲⫲ ⫲⫲⫲ ⫲⫲⫲ ⫲⫲⫲ /	36
2	⫲⫲⫲ ⫲⫲⫲ ⫲⫲⫲	15
3	⫲⫲⫲ /	6
4	///	3
Total		80

What percentage of the households in the survey had more than one pet?

Add the numbers of households that have two or more pets.

$15 + 6 + 3 = 24$

24 out of 80 $= \frac{24}{80} \xrightarrow[\div 8]{\div 8} = \frac{3}{10} \xrightarrow[\times 10]{\times 10} = \frac{30}{100} = 30\%$

Answer: 30%

Remember

Tallies are counted in bunches of 5, with a line across every four tally marks. ⫲⫲⫲

Test tip

In the test, questions about frequency tables may also involve calculating averages and range (see section K).

▶▶ Now try it!

1. The table shows customers' purchases in a music shop one morning.

   What percentage of the customers bought CDs?

   _____

   _____

Item	Number of customers
CD	24
DVD	32
MP3	15
Video	4

2. The table shows the results of a survey into the number of times people went on holiday the previous year.

   a How many of the people surveyed went on holiday more than once a year?

   _____

   b Approximately what fraction of the people who went on holiday twice last year were men?

   _____

   _____

Number of times	Men	Women
0	524	623
1	1 762	1 521
2	327	665
3	185	276

4 Bar charts

First read this ...

Bar charts use bars to show patterns in data.

The bars may be horizontal or vertical.

Both axes should have labels and the chart should have a title.

This bar chart shows some students' marks in a maths test.

The bar chart shows how many students achieved each score.

This is called the **frequency**.

You use a **double bar chart** to compare two sets of data.

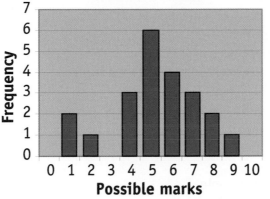

Class test results

> **Tip**
>
> For continuous data there are no gaps between the bars.

> **Tip**
>
> The vertical scale should start at 0 otherwise the differences between amounts appear larger than they are. This can be misleading.

Now try it!

1. This bar chart was produced by Freshco to compare the cost of a certain brand of cat food.

    a Why is the bar chart misleading?

    _____

    b What is the difference between the highest and lowest cost of the cat food?

    _____

Cost of cat food

(Bar chart: Cost in pence vs Supermarket — Freshco 62, Suppa Store 65, Low Cost 66)

2. This chart shows a shop's sales in May and June this year.

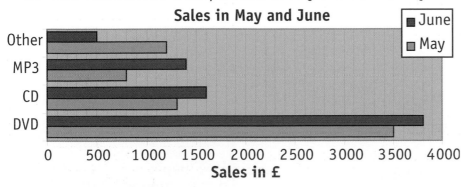

Sales in May and June

> **Tip**
>
> The key shows what the different coloured bars mean.

    a What is the difference between the total sales in May and the total sales in June?

    _____

    b Which item has the biggest difference between the sales in May and the sales in June?

    _____

First read this ...

▷ **Pie charts** show the proportions of different types of data in a set of results.

The 360° at the centre of a pie chart are split up according to the data being represented.

> **Example 1:** A tour operator conducted a survey of its customers' favourite holiday destinations. The pie chart displays the results of the survey.
> Spain was chosen by 150 people, which was $\frac{1}{3}$ of the people sampled.
> **a** How many people were surveyed?
> **b** What angle represents Spain on the pie chart?

a   The total number surveyed is $\frac{3}{3}$.
    $\frac{1}{3}$ of the number surveyed is 150 people.
    The total number surveyed = 3 × 150 = 450.

Answer: 450

b   The whole angle is 360°.
    Angle for Spain is $\frac{1}{3}$ of 360° = 120°

Answer: 120°

Remember

A pie chart does not give data values.

Favourite holiday destinations

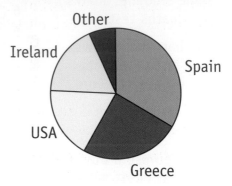

▷ **Line graphs** are used to display **continuous data**.

Points plotted on the graph are joined up with straight lines.

> **Example 2:** This line graph shows the temperatures in Manchester for the first five days in July. What is the difference between the highest and lowest temperatures?

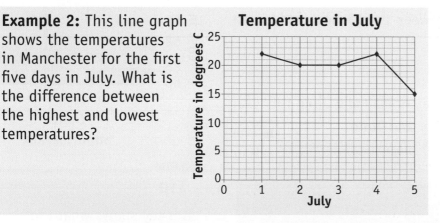

Temperature in July

First identify the scale. Five small squares represent 5°C, so one small square is 1°C.

From the graph, the highest temperature is 22°C and the lowest temperature is 15°C.

The difference is 22 – 15 = 7.

Answer: 7°C

Tip

You often need to compare line graphs that have been drawn on the same set of axes.

Tip

Line graphs are also used to display **grouped data**.
You plot the mid-point of the interval against the frequency.

Scatter graphs show any connection between two sets of data.

The scatter graph shows the marks of 18 students in a maths test and a physics test.

A point is plotted for each of the 18 students.

The points are grouped in a band that slopes generally 'uphill' from left to right, showing a connection between the marks in maths and physics.

Test marks in maths and physics

(scatter graph: Physics mark on y-axis (0–100), Maths mark on x-axis (0–100))

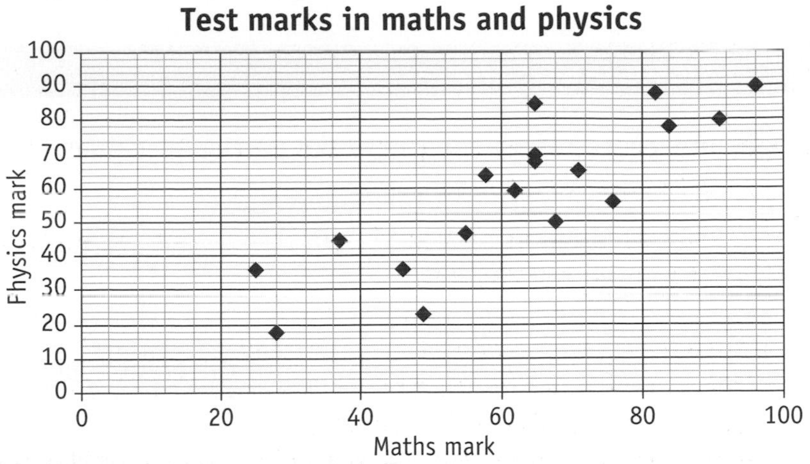

▷▷ *Now try it!*

1. The pie chart shows how a woman spends her wages. She earns £960 a month.

   a How much of the woman's wages is spent on tax and national insurance?

   _____

   b What fraction of her wages is the woman saving?

   _____

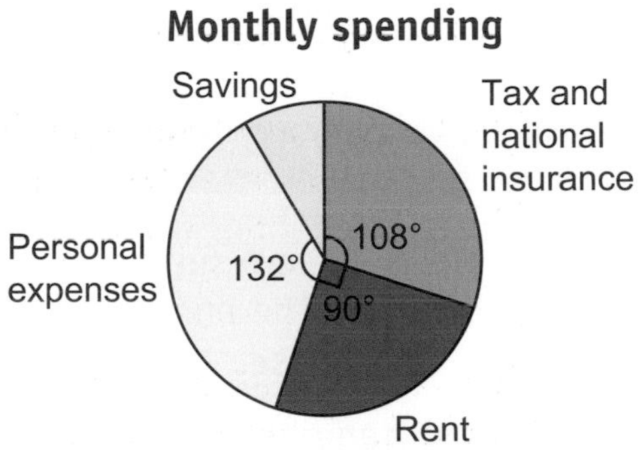

Monthly spending

(pie chart: Savings, Tax and national insurance 108°, Rent 90°, Personal expenses 132°)

2. A student heats up water as part of an experiment. He records the temperature every 10 seconds as shown in the table.

Temperature (°C)	40	52	65	79	85	92	100
Time (seconds)	0	10	20	30	40	50	60

   Which type of chart would you use to present this information?

   _____

3. This graph shows the sales of CDs and DVDs by a company in the first six months of 2006.

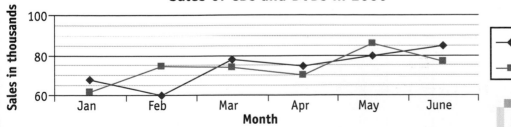

Sales of CDs and DVDs in 2006

(line graph: Sales in thousands on y-axis, Month on x-axis Jan–June; legend: CD, DVD)

   a In which months were the sales of CDs greater than the sale of DVDs?

   _____

   b In which month did the biggest difference in sales of CDs and DVDs occur?

Tip

It is not always possible to work out exact values from a line graph. In the question, the scale is too large to work out the individual sales for each month.

First complete this ...

▷ _____ data can only take particular values.

▷ _____ data can take any value.

▷ _____ _____ use bars to show patterns in data.

▷ You use double bar charts to _____ two sets of data.

▷ Pie charts show the _____ of different types of data in a set of results.

▷ Line graphs are used to display _____ data.

▷ _____ _____ show any connection between two sets of data.

▶▶ Now try it!

1. Here are the results of a survey on the number of TVs per house.

   How many houses had more than three TVs?

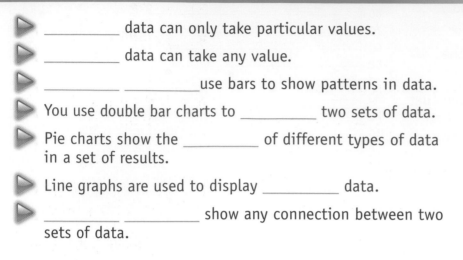

Number of TVs in the house	Number of houses
0	1
1	21
2	38
3	84
4	29
5	6
6	1

A ☐ 36

B ☐ 60

C ☐ 84

D ☐ 120

2. A travel company compares the number of visitors to major capital cities in June 2005 and June 2006.

A ☐ 22 500

B ☐ 25 000

C ☐ 63 000

D ☐ 61 000

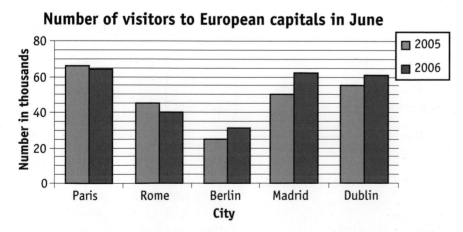

Number of visitors to European capitals in June

What is the difference between the numbers visiting Paris and Rome in 2006, to the nearest thousand?

3. Which city showed the highest increase in visitors from 2005 to 2006?

A	Rome
B	Berlin
C	Madrid
D	Dublin

4. The graph shows the sales for a shop in one year.

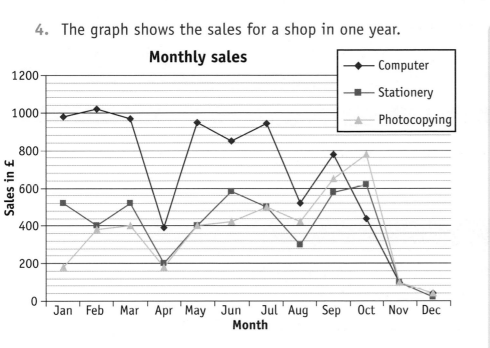

Which of these statements about the graph is correct?

A	the value of photocopying sales is lower than computer sales every month
B	the value of the stationery sales is higher than photocopying sales every month
C	the value of all sales fell and rose again in April and August
D	the value of all sales increased in June and November

5. The heights of 30 sunflowers were recorded. The results are shown in this table.

Height (cm)	13–15	16–18	19–21	22–24	25–27	28–30
Frequency	1	2	11	10	5	1

Which of these is the best way to present this information?

A	line graph
B	bar chart
C	scatter graph
D	pie chart

6. A company's profits for the first four months in 2006 are shown in the table.

Month	Jan	Feb	March	April
Profit (£)	1 790	1 840	1 735	1 720

The information is presented in a bar chart.

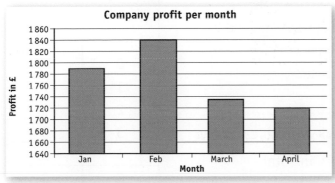

What is wrong with this chart?

A	The title is incorrect.
B	The axis labels are incorrect.
C	The vertical scale does not start at zero.
D	Some of the bars are incorrect.

K Working with averages

You should already know how to:

✔ find the mean and range for a set of data.

By the end of this section you will know how to:

▷▷ find the mean, median and mode and use them to compare two sets of data

▷▷ find the range and use it to describe the spreads within sets of data.

1 Mean

First read this ...

▷ An **average** is a value that is used to represent a set of data.

The **mean** of a set of data is the most widely used average.

▷ Mean = $\dfrac{\text{sum of values}}{\text{number of values}}$

> **Tip**
>
> An average gives a 'typical value' for the data.

Example 1: A student scores the following marks in her maths tests:

75%   77%   75%   48%   73%   80%   76%

Her friend has a mean mark of 75%. What is the difference between their mean marks?

Student's mean mark

$= \dfrac{75 + 77 + 75 + 48 + 73 + 80 + 76}{7} = \dfrac{504}{7} = 72\%$

Difference between the student's mean and her friend's mean

$= 75 - 72 = 3\%$

Answer: 3%

> **Tip**
>
> The mean may not work out to be one of the actual data values. Here, 72% is not one of the student's test scores.

You can also work out the **mean** of the data in a **frequency distribution table**.

Example 2: The table shows the number of pets owned by the occupiers of 25 houses in a street.

What is the mean number of pets per house?

mean = $\dfrac{\text{total number of pets}}{\text{total number of houses}}$

To work out the total number of pets, look at each category.

4 houses had 0 pets, this is $4 \times 0 = 0$ pets in total.

x	f
Number of pets	Number of houses
0	4
1	7
2	9
3	3
4	2
5	0

7 houses had 1 pet, this is 7 × 1 = 7 pets in total ...

The total number of pets

= 4 × 0 + 7 × 1 + 9 × 2 + 3 × 3 + 2 × 4 + 0 × 5

= 0 + 7 + 18 + 9 + 8 + 0 = 42

The total number of houses is the sum of the frequencies = 25

Mean = $\frac{42}{25}$ (× 4) = $\frac{168}{100}$ = 1.68

Answer: 1.68

Tip

Always check that your answer makes sense. The value lies within the possible numbers of pets, which is 0 to 5, and most of the houses have either 1 or 2 pets.

Now try it!

1. The heights of four boys are 151 cm, 154 cm, 162 cm and 153 cm. What is the mean height of the boys?

2. A man's journey times to work one week were 14 minutes, 18 minutes, 21 minutes, 13 minutes and 19 minutes. What was his mean journey time for the week?

3. An assistant chef makes 20 apple pies in 6 hours. He is paid £5.20 per hour. What is the mean payment per apple pie?

4. Five friends save £12, £10, £15, £11 and £16 respectively in a month. The following month, the mean amount the friends save is £13.40. What is the difference in the mean amounts of money saved for the two months?

5. A student has a mean test result of 65% for her first five tests. She scores 71% in the next test. What is her mean test result for all six tests?

6. Here are the results of a survey on the number of pets per household. What is the mean number of pets per household?

Number of pets	Number of households
0	49
1	56
2	16
3	9
4	5

2 Median and mode

First read this ...

▷ The **median** of a set of data is the middle value when the data values are placed in order.

To find the position of the median value in a set of data add 1 to the number of values and divide by 2.

Median $= \frac{(n+1)^{th}}{2}$ value

▷ The **mode** of a set of data is the value that occurs most often.

Example 1: A student sits seven maths tests. Her marks for the tests are 75%, 77%, 75%, 48%, 73%, 80% and 76%. The student sits another test and scores 78%.
a What is her median mark for the eight tests?
b What is her modal mark?

The test marks for the eight tests, in order, are:

↓

48%, 73%, 75%, 75%, 76%, 77%, 78%, 80%

a As there are eight test marks the median is in the $\frac{8+1}{2} = 4.5$th position.

So the median test mark is the mean of the 4th and 5th marks, 75% and 76%.

Median mark $= \frac{75+76}{2} = 75.5\%$

Answer: 75.5%

b The modal mark, or mode = 75%

Answer: 75%

You can also work out the **median** and **mode** of data in a **frequency table**.

Example 2: The table shows the students' marks scored out of 6 in a test.
a What is the modal mark?
b What is the median?

Mark	Number of students
0	0
1	2
2	1
3	5
4	3
5	4
6	4

a The modal mark is the mark with the highest frequency.

The highest frequency is 5 so the modal mark is 3.

Answer: The modal mark is 3.

b There are 19 values.

The median is the $\frac{(19+1)^{th}}{2}$ value = 10th value.

This is in the category where the mark is 4.

Answer: The median is 4.

Tip

median = middle
mode = most often

Tip

Remember to place the data in order to find the median.

Tip

If there is an even number of values, the median may not be one of the actual data values. The mode will always be one of the data values.

⏩ *Now try it!*

1. The number of chocolates in 7 tubes of Smarties was counted: 45, 46, 46, 45, 47, 48, 45.

   a What is the median number of Smarties in a tube?

     _____

   b What is the modal number of Smarties?

     _____

2. A survey of petrol prices recorded the following prices in pence per litre for unleaded petrol: 91.9, 95.38, 98.54, 91.9, 101.9, 108.9, 91.9, 95.38, 98.54, 101.9.

   a What is the median price of petrol in pence per litre?

     _____

   b What is the modal price of petrol in pence per litre?

     _____

3. The table shows the number of letters received by 40 households in one particular day.

   a What is the median number of letters received?

     _____

   b What is the modal number of letters received?

     _____

Number of letters	Number of households
0	1
1	5
2	9
3	15
4	8
5	2

4. The table shows the results of a survey into the number of parking tickets people had received in a city centre.

   a What is the median number of parking tickets for:

     i men _____

     ii women? _____

   b What is the modal number of parking tickets received for:

     i men _____

     ii women? _____

   c Use your answers to compare parking in the city centre by men and women.

     _____

     _____

Number of tickets	Men	Women
0	2	3
1	3	11
2	10	5
3	4	1
4	1	0

Tip

Remember that the mode is one of the values, either 0, 1, 2, 3 or 4, **not** the frequency.

Using averages and the range

First read this ...

You should choose the best average to use to represent data.

The table gives the pros and cons of each average:

Average	Advantages	Disadvantages
Mean	Takes all the data values into account	Is affected by extreme values
Median	Is not affected by extreme values	Does not take all the data values into account
Mode	Is not affected by extreme values	Does not take all the data values into account

Here are some common ways each average is used:

■ To find the typical number of goods produced per month in a factory, the **mean** is often the best average to use.

■ To find the most typical salary in an office, the **median** is often the best average to use, as it will not be affected by a few high wages.

■ For a clothes shop wanting to reorder stock, the **mode** is often the most useful average, as it will identify the items that are most likely to sell.

Test tip

You may be asked to **compare** sets of data using average values.

The **range** is a measure of the spread of the data. The range of a set of data is the difference between the highest value and the lowest value.

▷ Range = highest value – lowest value

Tip

The bigger the range, the more spread out the data values are.
The smaller the range, the more consistent the results.

Example 1: What is the range for this student's test marks?
75%   77%   75%   48%   73%   80%   76%

The highest mark is 80% and the lowest mark is 48%.

Range = 80 – 48 = 32%

Answer: 32%

Now try it!

1. The numbers of cars per hour driving through a village during daylight hours in a two-week period were:
12, 11, 12, 13, 15, 10, 14, 17, 16, 7, 9, 15, 12, 11.

Find:
a the median _____

b the mode _____

c the range _____

2. A student records the number of cars of different colours in a car park. The results are shown in the bar chart. What is:

   a the modal colour of car

   _____

   b the range in the number of cars of each colour?

   _____

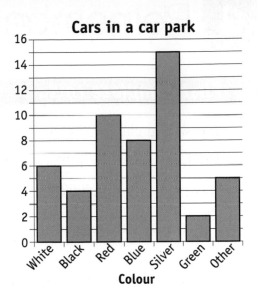

Cars in a car park

3. Which of mean, median or mode is the best average to use in these situations?

   a Witnesses to a robbery gave statements about the number of thieves who took part. Their answers were: 1, 2, 2, 3, 3, 3, 3.

   _____

   b Students were asked how long they spent watching TV at the weekend. Their answers, in hours, were: 3, 4, 3, 4, 4, 5, 10, 4, 3.

   _____

   c A manufacturer wants to know the typical number of sweets in a packet. Six packets had 102, 103, 104, 101, 102 and 105 sweets respectively.

   _____

4. The range in the weights of the male babies in a nursery is 1.8 kg. The range in the weights of the female babies is 0.7 kg. Decide which of these statements is correct.

   A Male babies are heavier than female babies.

   B The weights of male babies are more varied than the weights of female babies.

   C The heaviest male baby weighed more than the heaviest female baby.

   _____

5. A researcher counted the number of peas in pods, as shown in the table.

   Calculate:

   a the mean   _____

   _____

   b the median   _____

   c the mode   _____

   d the range   _____

   of the number of peas in a pod.

Number of peas	Number of pods
3	6
4	9
5	25
6	40
7	20

First complete this ...

▷ An _____ is a value that is used to represent a set of data.

▷ _____ = $\dfrac{\text{sum of values}}{\text{number of values}}$

▷ The _____ of a set of data is the middle value when the data are placed in order.

▷ The _____ of a set of data is the value that occurs most often.

▷ _____ = highest value – lowest value.

Now try it!

1. A baby's birth weight was 3.4 kg. In the tenth week, the baby weighed 5.3 kg.

What was the baby's mean weight gain per week?

A ☐ 0.19 kg

B ☐ 0.53 kg

C ☐ 0.87 kg

D ☐ 1.9 kg

2. The table shows the mean monthly temperatures in England and Wales, in 2004 and 2005, in degrees Celsius.

Year	Jan	Feb	Mar	Apr	May	Jun	Jul	Aug	Sep	Oct	Nov	Dec
2004	4.9	5.1	6.2	9.2	11.7	15.1	15.5	17.1	14.4	10.4	7.5	5.3
2005	5.7	4.0	6.8	8.6	11.0	15.1	16.3	15.9	14.8	12.7	6.0	4.3

What was the mean temperature for the year in 2004, to one decimal place?

A ☐ 9.8°C

B ☐ 15.3°C

C ☐ 10.2°C

D ☐ 12.3°C

3. What is the difference in the range of temperature in England and Wales for 2004 and 2005?

A ☐ 0.1 degrees

B ☐ 0.2 degrees

C ☐ 0.3 degrees

D ☐ 0.5 degrees

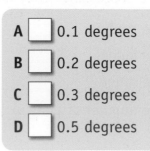

4. A café manager recorded the number of different flavour packets of crisps sold in one particular week. The results are recorded in the table below:

	Ready Salted	Cheese & Onion	Salt & Vinegar	Smoky Bacon	Total
Monday	11	16	12	5	44
Tuesday	8	6	5	3	22
Wednesday	12	18	11	4	45
Thursday	9	17	8	2	36
Friday	20	8	6	1	35
Total	60	65	42	15	182

What is the mean number of sales of cheese and onion crisps for the week?

A ☐ 3
B ☐ 8
C ☐ 12
D ☐ 13

5. Using the data from question 4, what is the range in the number of different flavour packets of crisps sold on Wednesday?

A ☐ 11
B ☐ 14
C ☐ 15
D ☐ 19

6. The marks out of 25 for twenty students in a test are as follows: 19, 6, 20, 21, 18, 22, 12, 15, 19, 13, 15, 11, 10, 8, 14, 21, 20, 5, 16, 12.

What is the median mark?

A ☐ 14
B ☐ 15
C ☐ 15.5
D ☐ 16

7. Fifty people were surveyed about the maximum amount they would be prepared to spend on a holiday.

The table shows the results.

What is the mean amount the people surveyed would be prepared to spend on a holiday?

Amount of money	Number of people
£5 000	2
£4 000	4
£3 000	6
£2 500	12
£2 000	16
£1 500	10

A ☐ £2 420
B ☐ £2 500
C ☐ £2 750
D ☐ £3 000

8. Sixty people were surveyed about the number of pieces of fruit or vegetables they had eaten the previous day. The results are recorded in the table below:

Number of pieces of fruit or vegetables	0	1	2	3	4	5	6
Number of people	2	4	6	10	8	22	8

What is the modal number of pieces of fruit or vegetables eaten by the people surveyed?

A ☐ 3
B ☐ 5
C ☐ 8
D ☐ 22

Answers to 'Now try it!'

A Working with whole numbers

1 Place value and rounding – page 5

1. 23 000 000 000   **2.** 250 (billion)
3. £22 600 000   **4.** 33 500
5. 3 988 000

2 Negative numbers – page 7

1. 17 degrees   **2.** −£145
3. £13 million   **4.** 87 degrees
5. £80 billion   **6.** 66 degrees
7. £55

3 Factors and multiples – page 9

1. a $2 \times 2 \times 2 \times 2 \times 2 \times 2$
   b $2 \times 2 \times 2 \times 2 \times 3$
   c $2 \times 2 \times 3$
   d $2 \times 3 \times 3 \times 3 \times 3$
2. a A and B
   b B, C, D   3, 5, 9
   c B, D   3, 9
   d none
   e A, B, C, D   2, 3, 5, 9
   f A, B, D   2, 3, 9
   g B, C   3, 5
   h B   3
   i B, C, D   3, 5, 9

4 Estimating and checking – page 11

1. £227
2. £2000 (£2392 for 52 weeks)
3. 15 (18.6)
4. 100
5. [£3] → [× 65] → [£195]
   [£3] ← [÷ 65] ← [£195]
6. [£25] → [× 6] → [÷ 5] → [£30]
   [£25] ← [÷ 6] ← [× 5] ← [£30]
7. [20p]→[÷100]→[×500]→[−£75]→[£25]
   [20p]←[×100]←[÷500]←[+£75]←[£25]

5 Tips for calculating – page 13

1. £4.63 [£13.37 [+ 3p] → £13.40 [+ 60p] → £14.00 [+ £6.00] → £20.00]
2. 3563 [437 [+ 3] → 440 [+ 60] → 500 [+ 500] → 1000 [+ 3000] → 4000]
3. a £134.50 [538 [÷ 2] → 269 [÷ 2] → 134.5]
   b 680 km [425 [× 2] → 850 [÷ 10] → 85 [× 2] → 170 [× 2] → 340 [× 2] → 680]
4. £8096
5. 52 [1432 [− 560] → 872 [− 560] → 312 [− 280] → 32 [− 28] → 4]

6 Remember what you have learned – page 14

1. D   **2.** B   **3.** D   **4.** A
5. B   **6.** C   **7.** C

B Working with fractions

1 Types of fraction – page 17

1. a $\frac{3}{4}$ **b** $\frac{3}{4}$ **c** $\frac{22}{25}$ **d** $\frac{3}{4}$
2. a $2\frac{2}{3}$ **b** $4\frac{3}{7}$ **c** $2\frac{5}{8}$ **d** $6\frac{7}{9}$
3. a $\frac{11}{16}$ **b** $\frac{13}{5}$ **c** $\frac{26}{7}$ **d** $\frac{43}{10}$

2 Fractions of quantities – page 19

1. 20 250   **2.** 450
3. £11 500   **4.** 48
5. £60   **6.** 7

3 One number as a fraction of another – page 21

1. $\frac{7}{10}$ **2.** $\frac{5}{8}$ **3.** $\frac{27}{100}$
4. $\frac{2}{3}$ **5.** $\frac{79}{120}$

4 Adding and subtracting fractions – page 23

1. 4 hours   **2.** $4\frac{1}{2}$ hours
3. $\frac{1}{2}$ hour   **4.** $1\frac{1}{4}$ hours

5 Using fractions to solve problems – page 25

1. £84   **2.** £84
3. £95 000   **4.** 16 mph
5. 625 cm   **6.** 20
7. 8

6 Remember what you have learned – page 26

1. C   **2.** C   **3.** D   **4.** D
5. D   **6.** B   **7.** C   **8.** B
9. C

C Working with decimals

1 Decimal numbers – page 29

1. 45 cm
2. a £0.019
   b £0.38 or 38p
3. 50 kg
4. 54.6 litres

2 Calculating with money – page 31

1. £65   **2.** £503.25
3. £11.71   **4.** £89.75
5. £253   **6.** 320 × 1.45 or 464 ÷ 1.45
7. £7200   **8.** $518

3 Remember what you have learned – page 32

1. D   **2.** B   **3.** D   **4.** A
5. A   **6.** C   **7.** D   **8.** C
9. C

D Working with percentages

1 Percentages – page 35

1. 72   **2.** 84   **3.** 63   **4.** 396
5. 300   **6.** 527   **7.** 176.4
8. 6.5

2 Using percentages – page 37

1. £1.20   **2.** £209
3. £2.75   **4.** £141
5. 30%   **6.** 27%
7. 20% (21.77%)   **8.** 65% (64.75%)

3 Percentage change – page 39

1. 34%   **2.** 25%   **3.** 20%   **4.** 5%
5. $33\frac{1}{3}$ **6.** 20%   **7.** 10%

4 Remember what you have learned – page 40

1. D   **2.** B   **3.** D   **4.** A
5. B   **6.** D   **7.** D   **8.** B

E Working with fractions, decimals and percentages

1 Converting between forms – page 43

1. a 0.8, 80%   **b** 0.15, 15%
   c 0.28, 28%   **d** 0.875, 87.5%
2. a 16%, $\frac{4}{25}$ **b** 32%, $\frac{8}{25}$
   c 8%, $\frac{2}{25}$ **d** 56%, $\frac{14}{25}$
3. a 0.64, $\frac{16}{25}$ **b** 0.24, $\frac{6}{25}$
   c 0.45, $\frac{9}{20}$ **d** 0.085, $\frac{17}{200}$

2 Remember what you have learned – page 44

1. C   **2.** D   **3.** A   **4.** A
5. C   **6.** C   **7.** C

F Working with ratio and proportion

1 Writing a ratio – page 47
1. 8 : 9
2. 7 : 8
3. 5 : 12
4. 4 : 5 : 9
5. 11 : 13
6. 1 : 7

2 Scaling quantities up or down – page 48
1. 225
2. 24
3. a 165 g of each   b 8 (7.7)

3 Calculations with ratio – page 49
1. £50
2. 24 kg. 108 kg
3. 750 g
4. 100 ml

4 Scale diagrams – page 50
1. 38 km
2. 13 metres
3. 4 miles
4. 7 cm
5. 1.6 m, 1.44 m, 1.12 m
6. 3 miles

5 Remember what you have learned – page 52
1. C
2. B
3. B
4. B
5. C
6. C
7. B
8. B
9. C
10. B

G Working with formulae

1 Formulae in words – page 55
1. £87
2. £145
3. 160 minutes or 2 hours 40 minutes
4. £355
5. £42
6. £46.90

2 Formulae in symbols – page 57
1. 2
2. 60
3. 27
4. 5
5. 54 cm^2
6. 5.12 inches
7. £75
8. 131°F

3 Remember what you have learned – page 58
1. B
2. D
3. C
4. B
5. D
6. C
7. A
8. C

H Working with units and scales

1 Time – page 61
1. 06.47
2. 26 minutes 17 seconds
3. 3 hours 35 minutes
4. 2 years 8 months
5. 1500

2 Temperature – page 62
1. 6°C
2. 0.6 degrees

3 Length – page 63
1. 4.25 m
2. 3.9 cm

4 Weight – page 64
1. 330 grams
2. 9.1 kg
3. 2.75 kg

5 Capacity – page 65
1. 140 ml
2. 25 litres
3. 72 litres

6 Conversion scales and factors – page 67
1. 2 hours 18 minutes
2. 55 cm
3. 19.8 metres
4. 27 metres
5. 65p
6. 200 g
7. 45 kg
8. 210 ml
9. 57 ml

7 Remember what you have learned – page 68
1. B
2. D
3. B
4. D
5. B
6. D
7. C
8. C

I Working with perimeter, area and volume

1 Perimeter – page 71
1. 60 cm
2. 22.2 m
3. 4 metres
4. 52 metres

2 Area – page 73
1. a 3.04 m^2 b 1900
2. 3000 m^2 (3014.01 m^2)
3. 8.2 m^2
4. 15
5. 2375 m^2

3 Volume – page 75
1. 144 cm^3
2. 48 000 cm^3
3. 7500 cm^3
4. 120 cm^3
5. 27
6. Internal measurements 9 cm by 9 cm by 3.6 cm high

5 Remember what you have learned – page 76
1. B
2. C
3. C
4. C
5. D
6. C

J Working with data

1 Reading values from tables – page 78
1. a £400   b £840

2 Types of data – page 79
1. a continuous   b discrete
   c continuous   d continuous
   e discrete   f continuous
2. a 192   b 1.70–1.79

3 Collecting data – page 80
1. 32%
2. a 1453   b $\frac{1}{3}$

4 Bar charts – page 81
1. a Because the scale on the vertical axis does not start at zero
   b 4p
2. a £500   b Other

5 Other charts and graphs – page 83
1. a £288   b $\frac{1}{12}$
2. A line graph
3. a January, March, April, June
   b February

6 Remember what you have learned – page 84
1. A
2. B
3. C
4. C
5. B
6. C

K Working with averages

1 Mean – page 87
1. 155 cm
2. 17 minutes
3. £1.56
4. £0.60
5. 66%
6. 1

2 Median and mode – page 89
1. a 46   b 45
2. a 96.96p   b 91.9p
3. a 3   b 3
4. a i 2   ii 1   b i 2   ii 1
   c Men receive more parking tickets for illegal parking in the city centre than women do.

3 Using averages and the range – page 90
1. a 12   b 12
   c 10
2. a Silver   b 13
3. a Mode   b Median
   c Mean
4. B
5. a 5.59   b 6
   c 6   d 4

4 Remember what you have learned – page 92
1. A
2. C
3. A
4. D
5. B
6. B
7. A
8. B

Published by:
Edexcel Limited
One90 High Holborn
London
WC1V 7BH
www.edexcel.org.uk

Distributed by:
Pearson Education Limited
Edinburgh Gate
Harlow
Essex
CM20 2JE
www.longman.co.uk

First published 2006

ISBN 1-84690-136-7
    978-1-84690-136-2

Edited and typeset by Ken Vail Graphic Design
Cover and text design by Ken Vail Graphic Design
Illustrated by Ken Vail Graphic Design and Beehive Illustration (Mark Turner)
Cover image GettyImages/Harrison Eastwood
Printed and bound in Great Britain by Scotprint, Haddington

The Publisher's policy is to use paper manufactured from sustainable forests.

◉ **Hot Topics CD**
This CD was produced as part of the DfES Move On project 2003–6 and carries Crown
copyright. Details of the Move On project and its successor Move On Up, commissioned by
QIA, can be found at www.move-on.org.uk.